ONCE UPON OUR TIME

For Tim Cook who believed

First published in Great Britain 2000 by
Glyndley Books and Craftsman

Text © June Counsel 2000
Illustrations © Marcus Sedgwick 2000

ISBN 0 9534232 2 0

Typeset in Perpetua

Glyndley Books
17 Andrew Close
Ailsworth
Peterborough
PE5 7AD

Craftsman
Beech House
Springholm
Castle Douglas
DG5 6RP

Printed in Hong Kong

ONCE UPON OUR TIME

JUNE COUNSEL

illustrated by Marcus Sedgwick

Contents

No Time

SIX o'clock and a bright Friday morning, everything waving and blowing, the clothes prop flinging itself backwards and forwards and Ellie Fugit, first out as always, battling to peg a sheet on the line. She'd got two corners pegged. The rest of the sheet billowed above her like a fat ballerina standing on tiptoe.

'Nail it on,' called old Mr Judd, pausing with his boot on his spade. 'Only way!'

Indeed it was a windy part of the world. Straight across the North Sea over the fens blew the east wind, nothing to stop it till it hit the village. Then it had something to play with.

'Oh!'

The sheet had tugged free. Up it flew to join the white clouds scudding across the blue. Free! But no, Ellie snatched it down. A laugh sounded the other side of the hedge.

'You look like a sailor struggling to reef the mainsail

in the teeth of a gale! Sailors call sails sheets. Did you ever read *Moonfleet* or *Treasure Island* or *Kidnapped*? I love sea stories, don't you?'

'Don't know,' called Ellie, spitting her hair out of her mouth, 'never read any.'

'Oh, but you should, you should. They're full of energy, like you. Can you remember what I said I'd call my talk tonight? And how long I ought to speak? I seem to have lost the letter.'

'*Lying for a Living*,' Ellie shouted, savagely pegging with her back to the hedge. 'Twenty-five minutes, then questions.'

'Thanks, I'm grateful. Better go and start.'

Ellie bent to pick up the empty clothes basket. Straightening, she looked at the washing having the time of its life on the line. No more satisfying sight could ever meet a woman's eye, she thought. It would be dry in no time and she could do the ironing before lunch.

She turned and went in. Baking next. My lemon drizzle or the new biscuit recipe or my famous fruit cake? Or all three? Yes, why not all three. She went swiftly into the bathroom, put the clothes basket on top of the empty linen bin, then hurried to the kitchen and began getting out baking trays, cake tins, pastry board, but was interrupted by a ring at the front door.

The post? So early? A parcel? None of those. Her Hedge Neighbour with a plant in one hand and three books in the other.

'Thank you for remembering the title of my talk and reminding me about questions! Oh, the dreaded questions!' She laughed.

She was a great laugher. It annoyed Ellie. Laughter was for jokes, comics, telly, not all the time and at nothing.

'These are the sea stories,' went on her neighbour. 'They'll take you away and away and away to wonderful places, and this makes the most gorgeous tea!'

Gorgeous was her favourite word. Everything was *gorgeous*. The most mundane things.

'You needn't do this,' said Ellie, shaking her head. 'I'm glad I could help, I've got a good memory.' And I don't live in a pigsty, she could have added.

'I've got a herb bed, I make herb tea, and I've no time to read!'

'I know,' laughed her neighbour, 'hence the gifts! Enjoy!'

She pressed the pot and books into Ellie's hands and

walked off, her laugh floating behind her.

That silly word, thought Ellie. Enjoy! It's all people think of now. *Do* is a better one. Then things get done. Things that need to be done. Enjoy comes afterwards, not first.

She pushed the door to with her shoulder and went down the hall to the kitchen and plonked the little pot on the windowsill. Hasn't she *heard* about my herb teas?

How could she live in this village and not know about my herb teas?

In the sitting room she put the books on the little table by Jim's chair, but they looked wrong.

They spoil the room, she thought. They're so old. They were, old and worn and shabby, and everything in the room was new and bright and shiny.

She tried piling them, but they were different colours and thicknesses and sizes. She tried fanning them, but they fanned clumsily. Well, lie there then, she told them angrily. I'll waste no more time on you.

She went into the kitchen and pulled her cookery books from their shelf (the only books in the house and the only bookshelf) and flicked over the pages trying to decide which recipe to do first. That woman's unsettled me, my Hedge Neighbour! Calling at this hour with sea stories. Pirates! She's a pirate, breaking into my morning, splintering my routine, blowing me out of the water! But I won't be sunk by a woman who can't even remember the title of her own talk, and she a writer! Oh bother, I *am* upset. Not sunk, but definitely all at sea. She slammed the book shut so violently the little plant on the windowsill jumped. She looked at it viciously. Tea! Yes, I could do with a cup and *you*, my friend, shall make it.

She put the kettle on, pinched a few leaves off the stem, put them in the small teapot. I should really plant you first and let you grow a little, but – your mother's annoyed me. She poured boiling water on the leaves, let them steep for a few minutes, then strained the tea into a cup. She took the tea into the sitting room and began to sip.

Her husband thudded down the stairs, went into the bathroom, showered, shaved, came out again, thumped about in the bedroom overhead, thudded down again to the kitchen, came out of the kitchen, and stood in the doorway of the sitting room, staring at her.

'Are you all right?'

'Yes.'

He waited. She went on sipping.

'Shall I get my own breakfast?'

'Yes.'

'Aren't you having any?'

She thought about this, then said, 'No.'

'You all right?'

The firm she worked for was in a bad way. She'd lately had her week cut to four days, and he wondered if the shock was getting to her.

'Perfectly.' She often smiled at him like that as if he was an idiot.

He went back into the kitchen and she heard him getting his breakfast. She poured herself another cup. Presently he called from the front door.

'I'm off now. Bye.'

'Bye,' she called, between sips.

She heard the car start, and go.

The phone rang. She put down the cup and went to answer it.

'Oh, Ellie, Patsy here,' (Patsy, President of the WI) 'Sorry to ring so early, but I knew you'd be up. Look, will you mind, I don't think you will, you're always so busy, if you don't make cakes as you promised for our charity coffee morning? You haven't started, have you? Probably you start in the middle of the night! Our new little member, the very shy one, wants to do it! She's been practising, bless her, and her mother-in-law's staying, who, she tells me, is a whizz at cakes, and she wants to impress her! What do you say, would you mind?'

'Well, if you don't want me to bake —' '

'Ellie, we adore your cakes as you well know! This is purely a matter of politics.'

'All right. My day is emptying fast.'

'What do you mean? *You* with an empty day! Pigs will fly.'

'So,' Ellie addressed the mixing bowl and the pastry board and the patty tins as she put them away, 'You can all have a holiday. We are not wanted.'

No baking left a hole in the morning and a hole in Ellie. She felt displaced, uncomfortable, edgy. Another cup, then consider. She boiled the kettle again, added a couple more leaves, swirled them round, and quite a respectable cup came out. She sat down to drink it. Hedge Neighbour, your tea is *not* better than mine, just – different. I'm not even sure I like it very much. Anyway, now the ironing.

She rose to go to the back door and found herself going to the front for the bell had just rung. If it's my neighbour with another plant or another –

But it was not. It was two Girl Guides, daughters of women in the village, shy, but determined. Why were they not at school? Oh, half-term.

'Good morning, Mrs Fugit, it's Good Deed Week. I expect you read about it in the parish magazine, or the paper. Please can you give us an hour's work? You put down the time we start and the time we finish on this form and sign it.'

'And how much do I pay you?'

'What you feel! You put it in this tin through the slot. We don't handle money. What would you like us to do?'

'What do you want to do? Or rather what can you do?'

'Anything! Well, not cooking. We'd rather not do cooking.'

'Dusting,' offered the younger one.

'I don't have any dust,' Ellie said, and she didn't.

'Hoovering?'

'I hoovered yesterday.'

'Perhaps,' suggested the older one, 'if we could come in and look round, we might see something that we could do.'

'Come in then,' smiled Ellie. There would be nothing for them to do, she knew that.

In the sitting room the girls looked round despairingly, till their eyes fell on the books. Immediately they picked them up, pounced on them, thought Ellie, and began to read. Without so much as a *by your leave*. Manners!

She stood stiffly waiting, but they went on reading.

'I've never read *Kidnapped*,' cried the younger girl, who was reading it, 'I've read *Treasure Island*.'

'It's more grown up,' said the older one. 'It's got sad bits. I cried over Ransome.'

They went on reading.

'Well,' said Ellie, 'that proves my point. I've always said reading's a waste of time. You two rang my bell, said you wanted to do a job, and look at you! Both with your nose in a book, and the books not even yours.'

'Oh, sorry, sorry, very sorry.'

They were flustered, the younger girl bright red with shame.

'Sh-show us the kitchen, please,' the older girl collected herself.

Ellie led them into her spotless kitchen, which could have been a show kitchen in a show house. She waited for their discomfiture, but they were staring through the window with joy on their faces.

'Ironing! We can do that. We do it at home. We love ironing. Where's your clothes basket? We'll fetch it in. Lots of it will be dry in this wind.'

'I'll do the shirts,' said the older one. 'I do my dad's when my mum's busy, and my dad's particular.'

'I'll do the handkerchiefs and pillowcases.'

'I'll do the sheets.'

'I'll fold, I love folding. My mum's shown me how to fold.'

Ellie opened her mouth to say no, *she* was particular about ironing, but remembered their mums. Impeccable women, immaculate housewives. If they'd taught their daughters to iron and fold, then they would be able to iron and fold.

'The clothes basket is in the bathroom on top of the laundry bin, but I don't think the washing will be – dry,' she told the empty air for the girls were already on the back lawn. She watched the elder girl lower the clothes prop, feel the washing and begin unpegging some of it.

The younger one took it from her and folded it neatly into the basket. They came in flushed and triumphant.

Ellie began, 'I'll get the ironing board – ' but they were already lifting it out from its corner, taking the cover off, unfolding the legs. They found the iron before she pointed and had it out of its box and plugged in.

'You go and have a sit. Have a rest, read the paper. Would you like us to make you a cup of tea?'

'We don't take a paper,' cried Ellie in exasperation. Never had so much work been snatched from her. 'We hear all the news we want on the radio or the telly.' And she read her boss's paper in the lunch hour, just the headlines.

'Cup of tea then? We'll make it.'

'No, no,' she cried, then yes, yes, she thought. 'But I'll make it. You get busy with the ironing.'

She put a tiny pan of water on the stove, rinsed out the teapot and pinched off the last few leaves of the little plant, even its tiny, tender growing top.

'Oh, don't, don't,' cried the younger girl, 'it'll die. Plants need their leaves. They can't live without them.'

'Pansy!' cried the older girl, already ironing. 'It's Mrs Fugit's plant, she can do what she likes with it. It probably doesn't mind all its leaves being picked. Come and fold. I've finished this.'

Ellie sat in the sitting room sipping her, what? Her fourth cup of tea! It's soothing, I'll give my Hedge Neighbour that. It's calming. This day is dissolving, time's spreading out all round me. I'm sitting in a great ocean of time, like a ship becalmed, not a sail in sight. In the doldrums.

She finished the cup and put it down, didn't rise at once to rinse it. Just sat, feeling time settling round her. A strange feeling. Little Pansy came in and took the cup and said, 'I'll wash it up. We're finished. Come and see what we've done.'

She got up slowly and followed the child. Pansy showed her the ironing, in the airing cupboard, neatly folded and put away in the right places. The shirts were on hangers, hanging from the shower rail. Silently she looked, but didn't praise, she felt too idle. Pansy led her back to the kitchen. The ironing board was back in its corner with its cover on. The iron was back in its box on its shelf.

The big girl, Cheryl, that was her name, Cheryl Strong, said, showing her an official-looking form, 'If you could just sign here, we've taken,' she looked at her watch, 'a bit more than an hour – ' An hour, good heavens, have I sat doing nothing for an hour? 'And, could you put, please, how you think we did the job,' Cheryl flushed.

'We did it all,' little Pansy said. 'I kept getting more dry things in.'

Ellie smiled. 'There are only two of us living here.' And wrote *Very Willing* by their names and put two pound coins in the slot of their collecting tin.

'Mrs Fugit,' Pansy looked up with huge eyes, 'could I borrow *Kidnapped*? Please. I'll take great care of it. I got the Booklovers Badge when I was a Brownie.'

'It's not my book, Pansy, it's my neighbour's. You must ask her. She's the other side of my hedge.' (Mr Judd was on the other side of a *fence*.)

'Ooh, I couldn't, I couldn't! My dad reads her. He says her books are really scary. They make the hairs on the back of his neck prickle. Oh, please, could you ask her to lend it to me?'

Ellie smiled as she held the door open.

'No! The library in town or the mobile library van will have it, or if they haven't, they'll order it for you.'

Pansy hopped about in agony. 'It's miles to the big library and the books I want are always out. The mobile takes for ever to get a book you order. Oh, please, *please* couldn't you ask her, *now*, I'll come – '

'Come on, Pansy, stop begging.' Cheryl was brisk. 'We've two more Good Deeds to do. Mrs Fugit can't lend a book that isn't hers and she hasn't time to go asking. She's a very busy lady.'

They left, Pansy still twisting her hands and arguing. Ellie laughed and shut the door. To want a book so much!

But a busy lady I am not. All my jobs keep disappearing. The bed! I haven't made it! Oh, good, the bed. She whipped upstairs into the bedroom and saw that Jim had made it, neatly too. He must have thought I was ill. She drifted downstairs again and wandered through the house looking for work, but no job shouted at her, none even whispered. Weeding, she thought, there's always work in the garden. She seized the little trowel and fork she kept by the kitchen door and went out joyously.

But – there weren't any weeds. The garden was as spick and span as the house. The wind was still in it, flicking the clothes prop about, but weeds there were not. Fool, she thought furiously, you did a huge weed yesterday after tea. Even groundsel can't shoot up in a night. She heard the phone ringing, and dropping fork and trowel ran in and lifted the receiver. It was Jim.

'Ell? Sorry to spring this on you, but I've got to go north again tonight. Big conference in Newcastle. The man who was going, can't. He's ill. So I've got to. I've got the old suitcase here, so I'll go straight from work, stay over, might be two nights, but one should do it.'

So, no cooking tonight, no meal to get. She made a few wifely noises and put the receiver down. This is very odd. No, it is not odd. Jim often goes north at a moment's notice. He often does. It was I who suggested his keeping a suitcase packed at the office. I packed it for him!

She wandered out into the garden again, empty handed. Empty handed! Empty altogether. Empty dayed. Anger seized her. She turned and went in, grabbed up the books, seized the plant and strode out of the front door. Good heavens, I never even shut it! But never mind. And round to her Hedge Neighbour. Her door was open. Ellie jabbed an elbow at the bell. The sound of rapid typing came from somewhere far back, and a voice called –

'Come in! Last door on the left.'

She leaves the door open! What a woman! Does she think she's immune? Ellie followed the sound of typing and came into a large room, door ajar, so cluttered, that she stopped, astonished.

Paper everywhere, books everywhere, cats everywhere, plants everywhere.

'Push something off a chair and sit down. I'm just coming to the end of a para, and it's been a *devil*.'

Coming to the end of a paratrooper, thought Ellie, disorientated. How long is a paratrooper? She pushed a cat off a chair and sat down. The cat leapt back and settled itself on her lap. Ellie sat, holding the plant in one hand, and the books in the other. Anger hot within her, but bafflement too.

The typing stopped. Her neighbour ran her eyes quickly over the page, then swivelled round to greet her, but saw the plant and cried, 'You've killed it! Used *all* the leaves!'

'Yes, it made four cups, very pleasant, but I *do make* herbal teas, you know. I'm quite famous for them in the village, and I do have a whole bed of thyme. There really cannot be a gardener in the whole of England who hasn't got thyme!'

'True, but there is only one gardener in the whole of England who grows *this* thyme as you must have found out. Swimming in time, are you not? Well, you'll spend your days killing it now. A deadly way to live. How about the books? Did you at least open them?'

'No, but little Pansy Readwell and Cheryl Strong did. They came round Good Deeding and the minute they saw them, they seized them and started reading. Little Pansy begged and begged me to lend her *Kidnapped*!'

Ellie laughed.

'Which you didn't?'

'Of course I didn't! How could I lend a book that isn't mine?'

'By asking. I live next door. We're both on the phone, or you could have called over the hedge. Even if I was in here, I'd hear you.'

Through the open window, Ellie could see the hedge.

'I was much too bus—'

She didn't finish the word. It would have been a lie. Her neighbour smiled. Ellie had never liked her laugh, now she found she liked her smile even less.

'You were not too busy. You never will be busy again. You have oceans of time to eat, sleep, wash, dress in. Nothing else. You may even stop doing those things.'

Ellie tried to speak, but found she could not. Her tongue was stiff in her mouth. She was stuck in the chair. The cat weighed a ton. She couldn't very well drop the flowerpot on the floor and there was no table to put the books on.

Her neighbour went on, she might have been reading the news, her tone was so sure.

'Your husband has left you. He's gone to his girl in Newcastle, she won't let him go this time. You have lost your job. A letter lies on your mat telling you so. You – '

Ellie broke in. The Jim bit was nonsense, so was the job bit. True, her week had been cut, but she was a key worker. They'd never sack her.

She said, 'So how do I earn the money to wash and dress?'

'You win the lottery, and spend it killing time. World cruises, buying houses, ranches, flats, drinking, drugging, marrying, again and again and again. You grow enormously fat and –'

Ellie said, controlling her anger, 'I came to give you

back your flowerpot and your books, please take them.'

Her neighbour laughed and stayed where she was. Ellie rose. The cat clung on with all its pins till the last moment, when it let go and fell to the floor, on its feet. Trembling slightly with anger, Ellie placed the pot on top of an overflowing wastepaper basket and the books on an overburdened stool, and walked out, her neighbour's laugh following her.

It was still in her ears when she reached her front door. A letter lay on the mat, hand-delivered and from the firm. She slit it open.

Courteously, with regret, it informed her that, owing to the pressing need to downsize even more, they would have, most reluctantly, to let her go. Had in fact let her go. A substantial redundancy payment would follow.

The words jumped about, the paper rattled, her hands shook so.

She remembered the boss's words when he called them in to tell them their week was being cut to four days, 'but only a temporary measure, ladies, till the recession is over.'

'I'll damn well go and see him!'

But the car wouldn't start. It had just been serviced,

but it wouldn't start. Bus then. She jumped out in fury, and walked down to the bus stop. Only a few buses ran from the village. A couple of early ones to get workers to factories and offices.

They were reliable. The later ones were not. She waited and waited till finally she said,

'Does this bus *come?*'

'Ha!' said one of the women who was waiting, 'driver's in his garden most like, picking his sweet peas. In summer he often has a pail by his seat and sells them to passengers. Gooseberries too, sometimes.'

Furiously, Ellie whirled round and walked rapidly back to the house.

She walked about the garden. What's happening? Everything is receding. She tried to think clearly, but the wind blew her thoughts about. She tripped over the clothes prop blown flat by the wind. As she steadied herself, she saw her neighbour looking over the hedge.

'Ellie, I need you!'

'What!'

'My editor's just rung. He wants another character! Says the book's too thin. My book *Voyagers*, which is coming out next year. I don't think it's too thin, but he's adamant, wants *one* now! I'm stuck, my muse has gone, lying on a beach somewhere in the sun, the trollop. I'm racking my brains, but they won't give. Come round and chat, talk, gossip, rave, whatever, strike a spark, get me going. Please.'

Ellie was poleaxed. First she insults me, then she asks a favour.

'No, I'm too b—'

But the word wouldn't leave her lips.

The laugh came over the hedge. 'You are not! You are the most unbusy person in the village. You are rich with time, spare me a little. Swamp me with words. Wash me off this reef I'm stuck on. I'll do coffee, biscuits. Come. Do. Please.'

Ellie lifted her eyebrows and went. At least, it's doing.

The room was slightly improved. There were no cats. 'I've banished them to the kitchen and shut the door.' There was a clean, but not ironed drying up cloth spread over the chair. The wastepaper basket had been emptied, the stool showed its tapestry top. A wonderful aroma rose from the coffee pot (silver, polished!) and a faint spicy smell from the biscuits. The china was old and beautiful, not a crack, not a chip.

Her neighbour saw her surprise. 'I've made an effort.'

'It's very nice.'

It was more than nice. The coffee was wonderful, the biscuits delicious.

'So, start. Anywhere you like. In the middle, at the end, dodge about. I shan't use it all, but I need to hear it all, that way what I do use will come off the page.'

'Off the *page?*'

'Publishers say that when a character's so real, it leaps off the page, lives outside the boundaries of the story, becomes part of the world's mythology.'

The words went over Ellie's head. She was sipping coffee, munching biscuits, frowning as old hurts rose in her.

'I don't need much.' Her neighbour's voice sounded anxious. 'It's a subsidiary character, like a walk-on part in a theatre. Do you go to the theatre?'

'No.'

'Oh.'

'My parents had me to look after them when they were old,' began Ellie. 'My mother told me *that* when I was five, and reminded me of it at intervals as I grew up. They were old when they married, didn't want children, didn't like them, but decided they'd better have one to take care of them when they were *really* old.' She paused. 'My mother trained me carefully in housekeeping, cooking, looking after them when they ailed. They didn't read, or go to theatres, or entertain. Church, crosswords, knitting, bowls and a week in Hastings in October when lodgings were cheap. But I planned to escape. And I did, poor Jim, I rather rushed him. And they are in a home now, and I don't visit.'

She smiled in triumph, then went on. 'I've never wanted children, though Jim did, and I do like a clean house, so I suppose I'm like my mother, but not selfish. I do a great deal in the village.'

She went on, her memory winding about, nothing like as ordered as her house. At one point she said, 'Are you taking notes?'

'Yes. Shorthand. Just some of it.'

After a time she stopped, looked at her watch. Heavens! Two hours? Have I been talking for two hours? No wonder I'm exhausted. Absolutely flat, and thin, nothing left in me. I'd like to lie down. Oh, I am lying down. She tried to get up. A breeze blew through the window and lifted her up. Hey, hey, I'm floating! Oh, lovely! Delicious! But a hand grabbed her down, plonked a weight on her.

'Here, here, can't have you floating off for some other scribe to snatch, just when I've got you all down.'

Ellie quivered with annoyance.

'You're shorthand at the moment, Ellie, but you'll be typescript soon, and then – print! You'll be famous. My books read well, I am a spellbinder. Aren't you thrilled? No more having to kill time, you'll fill time! The village will think you've walked out on Jim, because he walked out on you, and that the redundancy notice was the last straw. The police will look for you, but not find you. You'll go on the Missing Persons Register. You're no longer real to your parents, so they won't fuss. Oh, oh, nearly forgot, by the rules of my art, I must tell you the magic word.'

Ellie felt lips touch her, heard the whisper, then the laugh.

'If ever you hear a reader say that about you, you'll come off the page, assume flesh and blood, walk free!'

So there's Ellie, in hardback and paperback, on shelves and tables, in libraries and bookshops, homes and hospitals, and prisons; travelling the world in pockets and haversacks, suitcases and briefcases; read on board ships, on buses, in planes and trains; on beaches, on loo seats, in beds and bathrooms; by candlelight, firelight, torchlight, oil lamps, gas lamps, even, oh lovely, by moonlight; aloud, silently, in foreign tongues: written about, talked about, quoted. She often finds herself standing next to a famous classic or lying matily with a heap of modern masters. Never in a jumble, never in a secondhand bookshop. She meets *Kidnapped*. Cries over Ransome, falls for Alan Breck. Often hears praise for *Voyagers*. Sometimes hears praise for herself!

'Very well drawn!'

'Cleverly constructed.'

'Absolutely real.'

'My word, yes, I've met women like that!'

When she hears this, Ellie gets excited. The pages she's on rustle and quiver. Hope floods through her. Any moment now, they'll say the magic word and she'll walk and talk, stand among them. She listens and listens.

'True to life.'

'Memorable.'

'I found myself liking her!'

'I admired her.'

'I could understand her.'

'I must say I had a sort of sympathy with her.'

Nearer and nearer, now, now, now, thinks Ellie, ready to leap off the page, dance, sing, be human. The words keep coming. They talk and talk. She's very important.

'She makes the book,' someone says.

But they never say the right word.

They never say the magic word.

They never say *love*.

Stoned

THE bad boys were stoning a cat in the lane. The cat was bleeding, limping, trying to get away, but the boys ran after it shouting,

'Bingo! Got 'im, right in the eye!'

Something red and furious flew down the lane, leapt on the ringleader, clawed him, bit him, hung on to his arm.

'Get 'er off me! Get 'er off. GET 'ER OFF!'

The boys gathered around. One seized a handful of red hair and jerked it back savagely. The others saw a white face, eyes squeezed shut with pain, mouth stretched wide in agony. They all pitched in, got an arm to twist, a wrist to wrench, and pulled the girl off.

She looked a sight. Blood on her hands, blood in her nails, red blotches on her face, but the ringleader looked worse. Voices came up the lane. Women's voices.

'Christ!' swore the boys and fled.

The girl ran past the women, weeping with rage and pity, the women's remarks ricocheting off her like bullets.

'Did you see her? Like a wildcat! Blood all over her

27

face, fighting again. She is vicious. The schoolteacher says she can't control her. She should go to a special school. We've never had a child like that in the village before.'

'Born bad. Nothing you can do with born bad.'

This was from the ringleader's mother, who believed no evil of her son, though tales reached her.

The girl knuckled the tears out of her eyes, wiped her nose on the back of her hand and her hand on the seat of her jeans, then went after the cat. She knew where it lived. In a cottage that stood butt-end on to the lane with its thatch pulled down over its eyes. An old man with a bad reputation lived there. His neighbours had moved upmarket. Cars stood where front gardens had been. The long back gardens had been halved and sold to a builder to pay off the mortgage. Fancy names were painted on varnished wood or nailed to the wall in wrought iron letters. Amongst these poshed up pretties the old man's cottage stood sullen and unkempt, a piece of corrugated iron tacked over the front door to act as a porch, cabbages and potatoes growing up to the walls.

The girl was frightened, but not daunted. She had the spirit of saints and heroes. She pushed at the old man's gate which opened grudgingly and went round the back. There she found it, crouched under an elder tree that leaned against the cottage. The hair on its back was still dark with sweat and there was a red wound over one eye. She knelt before it, talking in soft tones, stretching out her hand. After a bit, the cat sniffed her fingers, then licked them. She stroked it gently under the chin.

'I'll come again when the old man's out. We'll be friends.'

Then she went home. News of the fight had reached her mother by way of the woman who cleaned for her.

'We've just come to this village for God's sake! We're trying to fit in, to be accepted. What do you think it's like for me to hear these things? You brawling with the village louts? What's it like for Daddy? Daddy in his new job, for your sisters at secondary school with the brothers and sisters of those boys you were clawing and scratching?'

The girl tried to explain what it was like for the cat, but the mother was in full spate.

'Every day I hear something bad about you. The other day in the shop –'

'If I could bring the cat here –'

'No way! No pets! I've said that. Our new furniture! Now if you want a pony –'

'I don't want a pony. The cat could sleep outside. I'd make a home for it –'

'It's *got* a home!'

'But it isn't *loved*.'

Her mother turned away in disgust. 'Outside or in, it's not coming here. You can't steal other people's cats.'

Later that day she said to her husband, 'I tremble to think where that girl will end. She is so violent, and she won't listen. She does not take one blind bit of notice of anything I say.'

When the mother was gone, the cleaning woman said kindly to the girl who was ranging round the kitchen moodily opening cake tins, 'Stay away from the cottage, miss, the old man can be very nasty. There was a young chap once who came out from the town to work for him and the old man knocked him about terrible.'

'What happened to him, the young chap?'

'Stopped coming! And serve the old man right. Why don't you have a pony? Your sisters are going to have a hunter each.'

'Ugh!' shuddered the girl and turned away.

She was rebellious and clever. She took note of the old man's comings and goings, when he went to the Post Office for his pension, when he went to the pub for his solitary drinking (no one sat near him, the village was afraid of him) when he caught the bus to market. Then she would slip in to succour the cat, bringing it bits of cheese, cooked fish, milk which she poured into a saucer specially bought for it at a jumble. She got a wooden box, put it under the elder tree and made it into a snug shelter protected from the weather.

'There, Prince, that's your sleeping place.'

One day the old man came home early from the market (had the village talked?) and met her coming down his path. He glared at her, but she tilted her chin and spoke first.

'Your cat's ill, he needs the vet. That wound over his eye has opened again or someone's hit him. I'll take him. I can pay the vet. I'd like to.'

The old man grinned a yellow grin. 'E don't need a vet. Cats heal natural. 'E's vicious. Look what 'e done to me.'

He bared his wrist, showed an ugly scratch. 'I give

'im a belt for that.'

He'd given it a belt before that, which is why the cat had scratched him, but he didn't tell that part of the story. He didn't stop her taking the cat to the vet, but he did go up to the house to complain to her mother, who complained to her husband.

'That disgusting old man came here! Rang our bell, stood at the front door complaining about her! I couldn't stop him. Thank goodness, no one was passing. He says she's been trespassing on his land, coming into his garden, feeding his cat, building it a shelter. She'll have to go to boarding school, she's got to learn how to behave. It's the only way, though God knows how we shall afford it.'

So the girl went to boarding school and life got tough again for the cat and tough for the girl who did not enjoy boarding school. It was a long way away, to the mother's delight. In the spring and summer holidays the girl went on school trips or to an aunt, but when Christmas came, she went home. Her father rather wanted her.

It was a Dickensian Christmas. The newspapers had pictures of farmers rescuing sheep from snowdrifts and motorists stranded on snowblocked roads. The girl put on her boots and went down the lane to the old man's cottage. Icicles like steel teeth hung from the thatch. She'd heard that the old man was sick and a home help came each day. She went round to the back and found the cat shivering in the box under the elder tree, and scooped it up. It was very thin, but purred immediately. She carried it to the cottage and pushed cautiously at the door. It was unlocked, for the home help, she thought, and went in. The room looked tidy, a fire had been lit. She could hear the old man's laboured breathing upstairs. She put the cat down in front of the fire, and stole into the kitchen. There was an open milk bottle on the table and a saucepan on the old gas stove. She warmed a little milk, poured it into the saucer she'd brought with her, and watched the cat drink. She warmed some more and watched it drink again, then sat down by the fire, took the cat on her lap, and murmured,

'There, Prince, now you're living posh.'

The cat told her in a velvet rumble that it liked living posh. They sat watching the flames leap up the black chimney while the snow piled up against the window. If

I could just stay here with Prince, thought the girl, like this, for ever and ever.

A car door slammed and a voice sounded. The home help, thought the girl. 'Goodbye, Prince.' She kissed the cat and went quickly out of the room, through the kitchen and out by the back door. She never saw the cat again.

The weather got worse that night, and worse still next day, and unbelievably worse the day after. Weeks of snow and struggle followed. Just to keep warm and fed took everyone's strength. Telephone lines came down, roads vanished under drifts. The village lost four of its old people that hard winter, the old man among them. His cottage did not stand empty, though. A man took it, but was often away.

The girl found the boarding school more unbearable than ever. She'd always had a rebellious streak. Now she rebelled in earnest. News came to the village that she'd dropped out of school; then that she was living in a squat in London with hippies; then that she'd written to her mother, 'I'm truly happy for the first time. The hippies are free people. We have no rules.'

'Huh,' sneered the village which had never known freedom, 'she'll learn. Life has rules if people haven't.'

They were right. The mind may be free, but the body is a stickler for rules. Her parents went up and tried to talk some sense into her, but came back without her. 'Leave her,' said her sisters, 'Let her learn.'

The family moved away. The village rather regretted them. The girl had always been good for gossip. Years passed. The village grew glossier, though not everyone grew richer. Those who grew poorer sank almost out of sight. The butt-end cottage in the lane was better kept, the garden spruced up, but the owner was hardly ever in it. 'Business, probably,' said the village. 'Overseas most like. You can see he's a clever chap. He's forever travelling.'

One cold May evening chilly as winter, the geraniums still indoors on windowsills, a woman got off the bus and came swaying up to the house where the girl's family had lived. She wore a shabby black jacket and a long stained black skirt. A cold spiky rain was falling. It fell on her spiky red hair and her dead white face. Snapped off lilac heads and tufts of double flowering cherry were strewn about the road and the gutters were choked with pink and white petals, such hailstorms and rainstorms there'd been. When she got to the front door she stared at it. The new owners had altered the garden, put in a new front door. She rang the bell, but they were out and no one came. She wavered across to the house opposite and saw over the heads of the geraniums, the heads of the family watching television, then she slanted back across the road to the house next door to the girl's old house, but this had grown so posh, it seemed to unnerve her, for she turned and went trailing on, crying in a messy way and talking to herself.

Once she stooped and picked up a bunch of lilac and a spray of cherry and carried them flopping against her skirt. There was no one about. It was not an evening for anyone to be about in.

She dragged on, biting her fingers, grinding the heel of her hand into her eyes to stop the tears, her thin body almost snapping in two as the mean wind blew through her. At last she came to the cottage in the lane. She stood a long time at the gate seeming to argue with herself, then her fingers found the gate, the latch opened willingly and she drifted up the path to the door and leaned her forehead against it, crying, and presently fell forward on to the chest of the chap who opened it.

He had a shock of black hair and a scar over one eye and knew her at once.

She was the girl who had kissed him free of the old man's spell and for whom he had searched, searched, searched till his money ran out.

Now he was broke and she was stoned and the last thing his resources could deal with was a sick woman, for the girl had broken the body's rules and broken herself into the bargain. But the heart has rules, too. Not as many as the body. Only one in fact. It must have love. So he picked her up and he carried her in and he gave her a lap and a hearth.

Mrs Spindle

ONCE upon our time, there was a secretary who longed to marry. Her hair was the colour of winter sunlight and shone like silk. Her voice was honey toned. When she spoke each word was like a note of music. Yet no man asked her to marry him. She was thirty-two and desperate.

She took to drinking gin in her bath. The hot water made love to her, the gin blurred her thoughts, while the tears ran down her face. 'I want to be married,' she told the taps. 'I want to be *adored*.'

One day she heard two typists talking in the Ladies.

'She's fab,' one said. 'I gave her my scarf and she said, "Your world will turn upside down. You will change cold for hot, and marry a man who's never seen you." And it's true! I'm going with Bill to Queensland.'

'But he's blind,' cried the other.

'So what?' retorted the first. 'I can see.'

'She's a witch all right,' went on the other. 'She put a spell on my spots and they vanished!'

The secretary asked them who they were talking about.

'Mrs Spindle,' said the typists. 'In Archives. You give her something of yours. She holds it in her hands and tells you all about yourself.'

The secretary laughed and left them. She walked to the lift, stepped inside, and pressed Sub-Basement.

The doors opened. Before her lay dimly lit, low ceilinged corridors. She chose one and set out, wandering past clumps of tall grey-green filing cabinets. She stumbled against bundles of old files done up in brown paper, and laddered her tights against the splintery legs of old chairs. When she was almost completely lost, she came to a door marked *Mrs Spindle* and went in.

The room was grey with steam and smoke. Old women were sitting hunched over piles of papers, muttering to themselves as they peered at file numbers.

One rose to her feet, shuffled over to a cabinet and pulled open a drawer. Another, who was standing by a boiling kettle, smoking and coughing, called out,

'Mrs Spindle, dear, are you having your own coffee or ours?'

The one nearest to the secretary looked up. Her skin showed her old like the others, but her hair was neither white nor grey, but glossy black and smooth. She wore a brown homespun dress and was hung about with necklaces of wooden beads, red, crimson, black, yellow and green. She raised her black eyes to the secretary and asked, 'Can I help you?'

The secretary found she couldn't speak. Her heart was thumping up near her throat. She took off her gold bracelet and held it out.

Mrs Spindle turned it round and round in long brown fingers.

'You want to be loved.'

'I want to be *adored*,' said the secretary. 'I want to be married to a man who worships me. Tell me what I must do.'

'I charge fifty pounds for counselling.'

'I can pay,' said the secretary, who was at the top of her grade.

'Pay me on your wedding day,' said Mrs Spindle. 'Now, you must make yourself ridiculous. Make yourself a hat out of paper, go to the park, take off your shoes and walk twice around the lake, but speak to no one while you walk.'

The secretary frowned as she took back her bracelet. She had a great sense of her own dignity, and dressed impeccably.

In her lunch hour, she took her boss's *Financial Times* from the wastepaper basket and walked to the park. There she made herself a paper hat, slipped off her shoes, put on the paper hat, and began to walk around the lake, carrying her shoes.

It was January, few people about. The ground was numbingly cold to her stockinged feet. A handsome man came up to her.

'Is it for charity? May I sponsor you? Let me carry your shoes.'

The secretary smiled at him but did not speak. He took her shoes and walked beside her. When she had walked twice round the lake, she sat on a bench and he knelt beside her, rubbing her feet until they were warm. Then he fetched hot coffee from the kiosk. She took off the paper hat and he stared.

'Your hair! That colour turns me on. Like sunlight on ice.'

That was the beginning and it didn't take long.

Under the winter trees they told each other their life stories. 'I've been too busy making money to get married,' he said. 'Had a few flings, of course, but now, now I want to get married.'

'I didn't want to in my twenties,' said the secretary. 'I loved my job. I wanted to get to the top. But now I do.'

'You have the most beautiful voice, did you know? I could listen to it for ever.'

She laughed and sang a snatch of song and he felt his heart stop in his breast. They were married in March. The sun shone, though the air was like ice. Mrs Spindle sent a card with Best Wishes and £50 pencilled in the corner.

I will send the fifty pounds tomorrow, thought the secretary as she posed for photographs, but on the morrow her honeymoon began and when it was over her husband said,

'No more London. I've bought a farm!'

So a new life began, so different from the old, a knife might have sliced her life in two. London seemed light years away, Mrs Spindle a dream.

'But I must pay the fifty pounds, nonsense though it is,' she said to her husband.

'Fifty *pounds*?' cried he. 'Fifty *pence* is going to be hard to come by. We're going to need every pound we've got.'

'Next year then,' said his wife. 'When we pull up.'

But next year a son was born. The man was over the moon to have a son. Now I shall keep him, thought the secretary, for the man had a roving eye and Mrs Spindle walked into her mind. You shall have your fifty pounds if we have to go short to save it.

Easier promised than done. There was no end to the things the farm needed. As soon as fifty pounds came together, it fell apart paying bills. The secretary began to make excuses. I would have met him anyway. He says he often used to go to the park. But Mrs Spindle fidgeted in her mind till one night the secretary turned on her pillow and woke her husband.

'Listen, I could sell my jewellery to pay Mrs Spindle.'

'Are you mad? Keep it. We might have a daughter.'

Nine months later they did have a daughter, a babe so beautiful, her parents worshipped her. The husband hung over the cot listening to her cooings and lifting her pale gold hair with his rough fingers. The secretary tried to be jealous, but could not, she was so happy. All this is due to you, Mrs Spindle, she acknowledged, and vowed to send the money, if not that day, certainly the next, or definitely the one after. But oh, with two babes and a house and a farm to look after, where did the days go?

A year came when everything they did went right. The farm prospered, the children, now at school, throve. From being almost bankrupt, they became almost rich.

'Now,' laughed the secretary, 'let us send Mrs Spindle a hundred pounds and be finished with her. Or at least fifty.'

'Or better still, nothing,' grunted her husband. 'She was an old con, probably a gypsy. She's damn lucky we don't prosecute her under the Witchcraft Act. You and I are going to have a glorious holiday. I'm taking you to Greece.'

To Greece they went (much of their money too): glorious, glorious Greece.

That winter influenza struck the land. The children caught it from school, the man caught it from them. The secretary nursed them all, till she was dazed with tiredness.

One night as she sat by the children's beds, she saw

Mrs Spindle in the fir tree outside the window. She was hunched up in the black branches, the moon behind her, looking at the children. The secretary started up, crying,

'No, no, you shan't have them. I'll send the money.'

Mrs Spindle vanished. The next morning the children were better.

When her husband had recovered, the secretary organised them to the coast to recuperate. They had help in the house and on the farm now, and could go away for short spells.

Walking along the winter beach with her husband, the children running before them, the secretary remembered she had never sent the money. She had been too tired. But I will when I get back, it will be absolutely the first thing I do.

She did. It was. Before she took her coat off, before she put the kettle on, she wrote out the cheque, wrote a note to go with it, sealed and stamped the envelope and walked back along the lane to the post-box. Dropping the envelope into the red mouth, she felt a lightness flood her whole body and was ashamed and amazed to find how good it was to pay the debt. I should have done this years ago.

'This year has been a magic year,' she said happily as the white peaks of Christmas showed above the horizon, 'and the best thing is I have finally paid off Mrs Spindle.'

He giggled. 'Well, actually, you haven't. The letter was returned 'Not Known at this Address'. You were out and I picked up the mail. I didn't show it to you, because I thought you might try again.'

'Oh!' said the secretary. 'Oh, I wondered why I didn't hear from her. She must have left the firm.'

She was annoyed with her husband and cross that the debt remained unpaid, but neither of these emotions ran very deep.

At least I tried, she thought. I did send the money. It's not my fault that it came back.

Stir Up Sunday came. The kitchen smelt of rum and brandy, dried fruit and spices. The children sat at one of the table making Christmas cards, the secretary stood at the other stirring the Christmas pudding. Once she thought of Mrs Spindle and laughed out loud.

The next day she walked in the woods with the children and the dogs. A thorntree, bent and brown, hung about with honeysuckle and bryony berries, red, crimson, black, purple, yellow and green, caught her sleeve as she went by. The secretary frowned and clicked her tongue.

'Oh, let go, let go,' she said as she freed herself.

That night in the hot kitchen, she could not get warm. Though there were a raft of things to do, she could not make herself start on any of them. She went to bed early, slept heavily, woke in the small hours and knew she was ill.

It was the new season's influenza, more virulent than the last. The secretary grew feverish and hallucinated. One night she woke suddenly with a terrible pain in her head and a dreadful pain in her throat. Mrs Spindle was stooping over her, one hand twisting her hair, the other squeezing her throat. She tried to pull Mrs Spindle's hands away, but could not. She arched her back and thrashed from side to side, but still Mrs Spindle held her until, presently, she took her hands away and left.

Nights of pain and days of weakness followed, till one grey afternoon the secretary sat up and saw a white-haired old woman looking at her from the mirror. Her husband entered the bedroom.

'Oh, good, you're better,' he said, but he did not kiss her, and he did not stay long in the room.

She tried to call him back, but some croaking bird had got into her throat and would not fly out. She put her hands to her head and felt the scalp barely covered with thin hair. In places she could feel no hair at all.

'It will come back,' she thought in a panic. 'As I get stronger, my hair will come back, and my voice.'

She got stronger, but her hair did not come back, nor her voice. The illness had taken both. The memory of Mrs Spindle standing by her bed returned to her. When she was strong enough, she put fifty pounds in her purse and without telling her husband went up to London.

A new firm was in the palatial office block, but the old doorman, who had always liked her, was still there. It hurt like a sword when he didn't recognise her, not even when she gave her maiden name.

'A lot left when the merger took place,' he said, answering her question, 'so many jobs were duplicated. But Mrs Spindle's not gone far. She's got a little antique shop just beyond The Bag of Nails.'

The secretary thanked him and turned away. She'd forgotten how big London was, the journey had tired her and her legs felt like rubber. As she came up to The Bag of Nails a craving for drink smote her so that she stood trembling for a whole minute before she could move on.

The shop was small and easy to miss in spite of the legend *Mrs Spindle* in faded gold letters on the front. The window was full of curios each with a hand-written price card somewhere near it, but there was a space in the middle.

As she looked, the brown velvet curtain separating the display area from the interior, parted and Mrs Spindle bent forward and placed a birdcage in the space. Her hair was still black and smooth, she still wore her rough brown smock and her wooden beads, red, crimson, black, purple, yellow and green, which swung forward as she stooped. She reached a hand behind her and brought it back holding a bird.

The secretary raised her hand to rap on the glass, but her gaze had been transfixed by the birdcage. It was, she saw, made of silk cords, stiffened somehow and gleaming in the dingy light. Like winter sunlight, thought the secretary, like sunlight on ice, and found her fingers touching her scalp.

Mrs Spindle set the bird on its perch and pressed it. The bird's body gave a tremor, its beak opened and it began to sing. The secretary gasped and her hand pressed against her heart. Mrs Spindle raised her head. Her eyebrows flew up. The secretary nodded and smiled. She fished out the fifty pounds and held them up laughing.

Mrs Spindle put her hand behind her again and brought it forward holding a card which she propped against the birdcage. The secretary saw the price. The smile fell off her face and she stood transfixed, still holding the fifty pounds aloft, staring at Mrs Spindle who stood smiling, gently playing with her beads and shaking her head from side to side.

The Goat Willow Tree

D ON'T be such a baby,' scoffed the little boy scornfully. 'Trees don't eat bread. They don't need feeding.' Here he was wrong, everything needs feeding, but he was only six. He was throwing his bread to the swan, but his little sister was bending down poking her bread into the roots of a tree. She always gave her bread to the tree. She was frightened of the swan and she loved trees. Also she did not believe her brother. The bread was always gone the next day.

'Leave her alone,' said their aunt. 'Trees need love and love is a food.'

They were in the aunt's garden (four acres, can you imagine?) feeding the swans on her lake. The children spent all their holidays with their aunt.

'Home now,' she smiled and held out her hand to the little girl.

There was a cake with pink icing and four candles which the little girl blew out, to her brother's jeers, in three goes. All her little guests had brought her presents and she thanked them prettily, but when her aunt gave her the little sapling in its pot, she could not say a word, she was so filled with joy. The boy, who always grew noisy and silly at parties, cried out,

'A willow tree! That's not a present! They grow everywhere like weeds.' He was repeating the gardener's grumbles.

'Not everywhere,' reproved his aunt. 'Not in my garden. This is your sister's very own tree. Come Sally, we'll go and plant it.'

She led the birthday party out through the French windows and down the garden till they came to a grassy piece where the gardener was waiting for them. There the little girl dug a hole with her bright new trowel and the gardener made it bigger with his old spade and the baby goat willow tree, *Salix caprea*, was planted, while the boy kicked up the turf and slyly made muddy marks on the girls' white socks. The aunt and the gardener, Mr Roots, put a little tube of wire netting around the tree to protect it.

'Will it be all right?' the little girl asked anxiously.

'The soil is right, plenty of water, the position is right, open and sunny, but what life does to it and what the tree does about what life does to it, that we shall have to see,' said the aunt.

She led them back to watch the conjuror, then they played games that Sally chose till her brother got so obstreperous he was sent to bed and soon after that the party finished. From her attic window (the attics were cosier than the big bedrooms below) Sally looked out and saw her own willow tree in the clear spring dusk with its protective tube around it, out of its pot for the first time.

There were many mature trees in the aunt's garden. A cedar, its lower limbs lopped decades ago, stood within yards of the dining room window.

'That needs to come down,' visitors said. 'It takes all your light.'

To which the aunt replied, 'I have light enough. I am not a lace-maker or a weaver.'

There was a beech so huge it was like a small town. There was an ash tree which came into leaf so late every year that they thought it had died. Not until late June did its feathery fans show, not until July did the crown thicken and green. There was a bluebell walk through silver birches so beautiful it was like music. There was a mountainous chestnut tree. 'Planted in my great-grandfather's top hat in a pond that stood there,' the gardener told. Its roots had long ago sucked up the pond. It had a twisted green trunk, branches that swooped down, then up to give the coolest thickest shade in summer. And, in a field beyond the garden, there was a grove of cricket bat willows that brought the aunt a little pocket money and helped a small firm to survive. Amongst all these titans the *Salix caprea* had no rank at all. It was planted for love, and with love it grew.

On her seventeenth birthday Sally had a picnic under her tree. There was a white cake on a white cloth with *Salix caprea* drawn on it in delicately coloured icing, and seventeen yellow candles. She and her aunt and her brother drank pale bubbling yellow wine in tall glasses.

'To Sally and her tree!'

The gardener got up with his cake in his hand and wandered among the fruit trees he and the aunt had planted to dry up the boggy half-acre . Sally knelt down and poured wine from her glass into the goat willow's roots and pushed in a thin slice of cake. The young willow waved its slender grey branches against the bright blue sky and trafficking across and in and out and up and down them flew hundreds of bees, merchandising among the bright gold catkins. It looked like an airy city with shining narrow grey streets winding and crossing beside canals and lakes of brilliant blue. So thought Sally, lying underneath, looking up.

She was a long girl, long limbs, long face, long nose, long neck, long hands, long feet, even long toes. Her eyes were blue and dreamy, her hair (long) was the colour of the catkins above.

The young man drawing beside her thought her beautiful. He was a friend of her brother's and studying to become an architect, and as full of dreams as Sally. He wanted to build beautiful homes for people, plan beautiful towns. The aunt sat in her garden chair and watched them. The brother lay on his stomach pulling up grasses and popping small beetles between his thumbnails. Suddenly he spoke.

'When are you going to sell this place, Aunt? Now would be a good time.'

The aunt started and plucked at her yellow neck. 'I shan't sell! I shall live here till I die, and afterwards, only more comfortably, because I shall be out of my body.'

Her body was not comfortable now. It was an effort

to garden, an effort to do most things.

'Marcus, why did you say that?' stormed Sally when they were back in the house. 'It was a vile thing to do. You saw how it upset Aunt.'

'Aunt can't go on for ever,' drawled her brother. 'This place is too big. She'll have to go into sheltered housing sometime. Why not now?'

The aunt had gardened too long to be upset by her nephew's behaviour. Life would teach him a thing or two, and soon. She was sitting in the dining room listening to his friend, the student, expound his dreams. The picture he had drawn of Sally lay under her hand and her fingers tapped it gently as she watched his waving hands, his shining eyes.

'I have a dream I'd like turned to stone,' she said when he stopped and told him that when she was a child she had longed to walk into the morning from her bedroom window just straight into the shining air.

'I still want to do that,' she said. 'It's the only thing I do still want to do.'

'Like this,' said the student, holding up a sketch of a narrow bridge arching from a balcony. He had started to draw as soon as she started to talk. He could catch fire from other people's dreams as well as his own.

'Where would you like it to end?' he asked. 'It must go somewhere. What tree would you like it to end in?'

'In Sally's willow,' replied the aunt thoughtfully. 'That would be strong enough by the time you are ready to build. I should like to sit in its branches and listen to it.'

'Do you know what our mad aunt's suggested to Stephen?' raved the brother to the sister. 'Do you know what she's agreed to pay him? What they think the materials and labour will cost? It's our money she's wasting, and your tree that will be cut about. If you don't care about our money, think about your tree.'

'My tree won't mind,' said Sally dreamily. 'It can spare a branch or two. Stephen won't cut any branch that doesn't need to be cut. Aunt's not well, why shouldn't she have a dream come true?'

So the folly was built. A little white house on stilts like a stork, with a covered outside staircase to the first floor and a narrow bridge, just wide enough for one, trembling through the air from a wrought iron balcony to the heart of the goat willow tree. It was a springy bridge, but quite safe, and went some twenty metres supported on two slender poles. It ended in a small sheltered seat in the arms of the tree. It took a lot of designing, a lot of time, a lot of money and a lot of fighting (for the planning committee was very dubious), but when it was done it lifted the heart to look at it, as a dream should do.

The aunt moved in and gave a small party. She presented the student with a handsome cheque, the gardener popped the champagne and Sally gave the toast, 'To Aunt and her Willowbridge!' Then she went down the outside staircase with the student and through the orchard to the goat willow tree and both of them poured champagne on its roots. The student gave her a fine gold chain with a leaf from the goat willow tree dipped in gold hanging from it. Standing with their arms around each other, lost in the whispering tree, neither of them heard the furious row that raged in the room behind the balcony.

The next morning the gardener swept up the broken glass and the aunt sent for her nephew who came in his own good time, sulking and savage.

'I am not asking for apologies,' said she. 'I know you feel cheated. So I have decided to bring forward your inheritance. I shall make the big house and land over to you, reserving only a small annuity for myself, a pension for Mr Roots, and the half-acre that this house stands on.'

'And what does Sally get?' sneered the young man.

'Nothing,' replied the aunt. 'Sally has beauty, love, grace and goodness, plenty to make her way with.'

'I don't believe you,' scowled her nephew, but fairly soon he had to for the big house with its four-acre garden and the field with the cricket bat willows became his. The only thing that did not become his was the Willowbridge House and the half-acre it stood on. Sally was pleased. She knew that her aunt would be free from responsibility and the old gardener would be secure and she believed her brother would be happy.

He was at first. He bought a fast car, went up to London, got a job in advertising, then a job in television, then a job in a travel company. The student passed his exams and became an architect of promise and, because of Willowbridge House, performance. The aunt's folly had been written up in the glossy magazines and now rich people and pleasure park owners vied for his services.

'A few years of this,' he said to Sally, 'and I can do the serious designing I really want and we can be married.'

'Yes,' sighed Sally blissfully. She had absolute trust in

him, wanted to stay near her aunt, and was in no hurry to be married, being a slow developer. She moved into Willowbridge House. The gardener, whom the brother had fired, built himself a hut in the half-acre and looked after the orchard.

The first year was magical. Every morning the aunt walked into the morning across the bridge and sat in her special seat. The second year was not so good. She found she could only walk into the morning in fine weather: in bad weather she had to sit on the balcony, and in very bad weather, in her bedroom. But whatever the weather she talked to the willow tree and the goat willow listened. The third year began both good and ill. Stephen was making money and a good name for himself. Marcus was losing money and making a bad name for himself. The aunt discussed them both with the willow tree.

'Stephen should marry Sally. He's made money enough. Marcus has no brakes. He over-reaches himself and I don't like the friends he's collecting. What? What? What do you say?'

For the willow was rustling agitatedly. She walked out on to the bridge and listened. The morning was misty. Sounds were diffused and muffled, but even so, she called Sally, sharply.

'Sally, Sally, get on your bicycle, go up to the big house and see what is happening.'

Sally went pedalling up. When she got there she was stunned. The big cedar was down, scaffolding was up, the garden was carved into deep yellow ruts. Marcus was talking to a man in a safety helmet, who wore an orange jacket.

'Hi, Sal,' said he indifferently as she got off her bike.

'Marcus, what are you doing?'

'What's it look like?' The man beside him looked up sharply at his rudeness, Marcus altered his tone. 'I've formed a company, Marcus Homes, to develop the estate.'

Sally felt as though he'd struck her with an axe. When she recovered he and the man had moved away, so she pedalled straight to the village phone box and rang Stephen.

'Don't panic, Sally, it needn't be a disaster. People have got to have homes. I'll come down and talk to Marcus.'

He came down. 'I'm tired of building silly fantasies for rich people, I'm longing to do some real work. Let me design your estate, Marcus, we could make it sensational. We'll have posh homes, small homes, sheltered housing, shops, a community centre. I'll plan it around the trees, they're glorious, and I'll do it for peanuts, well, almost, for love anyway.'

He waved his hands, his eyes shone. Marcus stared at him. 'I believe you would. All right, you're on, but the Board's decision is final, we reserve the right to make any necessary alterations.'

'Understood,' said Stephen. 'That's usual.'

Sally felt comforted. It would be lovely to have Stephen near her and exciting for Stephen to be doing what he wanted to do. She said, 'Marcus, you must come and see aunt and say you're sorry about not telling her first. It was a dreadful shock, especially about her beloved cedar.'

'But I'm not sorry,' said her brother, 'a tree down is money for Marcus.'

At first all went well. The Board accepted Stephen as architect and Stephen went to work with enthusiasm, idealism and talent, not to mention love. His plans were passed, the houses began going up, but perversely, the same qualities that would bring Marcus money and fame, also aroused his jealousy. He was jealous of

Stephen, the whiz-kid wonder, and also, he saw that if he knocked out the idealism, he could make more money. So the rows began.

'What insensitive fool gave the order to fell the ash tree?' demanded Stephen. 'It was needed to give height to the vista, not to mention something the children would enjoy.'

'Sorry, old chap, it was the Board's decision. They were afraid it would die in a year or two and then it would have to come down anyway.'

'I see the Board have used the space to put another house in,' said Stephen acidly. 'I trust the Board will allow the chestnut tree to stand. The village green I've designed will be nothing at all without the chestnut tree.'

He was furious, but not surprised, when the Board vetoed the chestnut tree and built houses on the green.

He told Marcus fiercely, 'The Bluebell Walk *must* stay. I won't bore you with the pleasure it will give people, just remind you that it will help to sell your posh houses. And Sally loves it. Doesn't that move you?'

Unfortunately it did. Sally and Stephen's glowing love showed up all the thin places in Marcus's marriage (to a purple-haired woman who hated the country).

The Bluebell Walk was cut down and a mean street of cramped houses built where it had been.

'That's it,' swore Stephen. 'I'm resigning. Do you know he wants to drain the lake?'

'Oh, don't go, don't go,' Sally begged. 'If you leave he'll murder the estate.'

So Stephen stayed, but the joy had gone. Marcus *did* drain the lake, which was a small one, and turned it into a swimming pool for the big house, denying its amenity to the rest of the estate. The aunt entered the conflict. 'You cannot cut down the beech tree,' she informed her nephew coldly. 'It is one of the oldest beech trees in England and is protected.'

But not strongly enough, for Marcus did cut it down. Stephen had designed sheltered housing around a courtyard in the middle of which stood an almond tree so lovely, so fragile, so hopeful, he smiled as he drew the plans. Marcus cut it down and squashed in more houses.

'At least the cricket bat willows will survive,' sighed the aunt. 'He'll never cut himself off from income.' But that income was peanuts compared with what Marcus was getting from selling houses, so down came the cricket bat willows and the family firm that depended on them went bust.

The estate was finished. There was not a tree left, but all the streets had names like Bluebell Walk, Chestnut Crescent, Beech Way, Cricket Bat Grove (which was thought very quaint). Marcus was very rich, but jealousy, envy and greed are restless companions. He thought of one last thing to do.

'No,' said his aunt sharply. 'I will not and if you try I shall go to law and spend my last penny suing you.'

He had tried to buy her half-acre and when she refused said the goat willow tree stood on his land and that he would cut it down. Her fierceness made him pause. There had been a scandal over the beech and his Board would not want another burst of bad publicity. So he tried to hassle his aunt out of her new house. He sent men to cut down the willow at night, to burn it down, to stuff it with rubbish. The men came back cut about the face as though they'd been whipped, one almost blinded. The willow would not burn, though their trousers had. The rubbish was hurled mysteriously out again and landed in the posh gardens.

'I realise that you aren't sorry about the trees, but you've upset Aunt, broken Mr Roots' heart, nearly made Stephen have a breakdown, you *must* be sorry for all *that*,' said poor Sally, bewildered by badness.

'But I'm not,' replied her brother blithely. 'All these things would have happened sooner or later, why not now?'

He and his purple wife gave a party in the big house to celebrate the finishing of the estate. The Board came. Sally and her aunt stayed away. Stephen had already left for the north where he was designing a tower for a dotty millionaire. He didn't even marry Sally. He was bitter, disillusioned and wanted to take the taste of the last eighteen months out of his mouth. Sally bicycled daily through the estate to her cookery and embroidery classes and tried not remember the old friends that had stood there.

So time went on. The purple wife spent Marcus's money. The Board members bickered amongst themselves. The people of the estate gave parties, swapped wives, commuted. The gardener planted a thick hedge round the half-acre.

Sally cooked, shopped, bicycled, embroidered, ran the home, helped in the garden and fell into bed at night. The last thing she always did was to hold the gold willow leaf between her fingers and send her love to Stephen.

Then, things began to go wrong in the estate. Houses began to tilt and sink, floors began to rot, gardens to squelch and squirt and, in spite of central heating, spitty chesty coughs sounded from bedroom after bedroom. The residents, who were mostly top level executives, articulate, vociferous and, some of them, powerful, formed an association and bombarded the Board. The Board looked to Marcus, who ordered his advisers to look into the matter. They did.

'Well?' he snapped.

'Trees,' they replied.

'Trees,' he glared. 'What do you mean *trees*? There aren't any trees.'

'That's the trouble,' they said. 'There should be. You built on land with a lot of water underneath. When the trees were there, they drained it. Now the water's coming back. You should have left the trees.'

The press took the matter up and photographed the rotting houses. Television sent its interviewers down. Marcus consulted his lawyers. The residents consulted theirs. The next year was wet beyond all records (even for England). A snow-filled winter, a rain-drenched spring, a soaking summer, then autumn, season of mist and yellow (and green) mouldiness. The pond where the chestnut tree had been planted reappeared in somebody's drawing room. The brook that had wandered through the Bluebell Walk now meandered through the mean street in and out of the cramped houses. The stream the cricket bat willows had leaned over rose again in a line of garages. The swimming pool remembered it had been a lake.

Sally dreamed a green dream. *Salix caprea* stood by her bed and said, 'Get up, Sally. Come down and feel amongst my stems.' It gave her one last instruction, then faded. She leapt out of bed, dressed, ran down the outside staircase and found the first two steps were under water. She splashed down the garden and met Mr Roots wading towards her with his storm lantern in his hand. 'Stay with Aunt, please,' she cried as she splashed on. She knelt in the slopping water and felt amongst *Salix caprea*'s many stems. Her fingers grasped something with a hard, curved edge and she hauled it out. By the light of her torch she saw it was a small round boat made of woven willow boughs covered with hide like a Welsh coracle. Who had made it? Mr. Roots? No time to wonder. She got in and immediately, without push or paddle, it sped off. The street lights were out, but the sound and smell of water was everywhere. Cries and lamentations sounded from all sides.

In the upstairs rooms of dark houses figures scurried to and fro with lighted candles. Down the streets which were now waterways the willowboat bobbed till it fetched up at the big house and bumped against the door. Immediately the door opened and the boat sailed across the hall and stopped at the fourth stair. Sally stood up and shouted, 'Marcus, Marcus!' He came, a lighted candle in a silver candlestick in his hand, hair on end, mouth ajar.

'Marcus, I've a message from the willow tree. If you will put your hand on its trunk and say you're sorry, the waters will go down. If you don't they will go on rising. One little word to the tree, Marcus, that's all. No-one will hear you, no-one will see you, but you must come *now*.'

She held out her hand to him. He smote it away.

'Are you mad? I'm not sorry. Stephen's the one to blame for this. He's the architect. He designed this estate. His name's on the plans, on the contract. He'll be the sorry one, I'll see to that.'

The boat spun round and shot out of the door so fast

it nearly overbalanced Sally. She tried to steer it towards some of the houses but it would not turn. It did pause, however, for her to rescue a desperately swimming dog, and again for a terrified cat, and once more for a budgie trapped in its floating cage. Then it bobbed on till it bumped against the outside staircase of the aunt's house. The water was over the third step. Sally ran up the steps, the cage in her hand, the cat and the dog following. In the drawing room the gardener and the aunt had lit candles. The little house was trembling, ornaments and pictures rattling. Sally remembered how uncomfortably, and deliberately, close Marcus's last building operations had been. Had the foundations for the stilts been shaken? The floor tilted. They clung together.

'Quick,' she cried, 'over the bridge to the tree.'

The aunt took the cat, the gardener the dog, in single file they walked into the night over the shaking bridge. The aunt settled herself in her seat with the cat on her lap. The gardener hunched himself into the branches with the dog under his arm, Sally stood upright, winding her long limbs through the branches, holding the birdcage. The aunt stroked the cat and prayed. The gardener sucked on his pipe. Sally put her free hand inside her shirt and gripped the gold willow leaf. Stephen, Stephen, Stephen, she called silently.

They listened to the slap and push of water beneath them, the distant cries and shouts. The dark hours went by, the water rose. When the eastern sky began to lighten, they saw the water make a rush at one of the stilts. It slipped from under and the house hung dipping. The water rushed again, a second stilt broke. The house swung round pulling at the bridge. *Salix caprea* braced itself and leaned back. Then began a tug of war between the tree and the house. The bridge broke off and the house swam away trailing the bridge behind it.

The sun rose and shone on families sitting on rooftops wrapped in blankets. The joke was that many of them had boats in their second garages. One family snorkelled their way into the garage and got the boat out. In it they set sail for Marcus's house. He saw them coming, at first laughed, then changed colour. He was not afraid of an argument, but their expressions were not so much argumentative as murderous. He ran to the back of the house, dived out of the bathroom window and swam for his aunt's house. He was a good swimmer and the current was flowing strongly towards the half-acre.

The sun rose higher and shone with its full strength. The waters were still rising, but a wonderful sound had entered the sky and was coming towards the willow tree. The branches parted to let Sally see.

A helicopter was coming. The dotty millionaire (a man in a million) was at the controls with Stephen beside him. Stephen saw Sally and waved. Then came the difficult business of pulling up the aunt and the cat, the gardener and the dog, and long, strong Sally with the budgie.

'I do believe that *Salix caprea* is helping,' gasped Stephen as he struggled. 'It's stretching up and holding you steady. I had a dream about you last night that you were in danger. I told Mike here and he said, "Let's go see."'

Off they went, saved and happy, and the noise of the helicopter drowned the sound of Marcus shouting for help. He had arrived at *Salix caprea*'s lower limbs and was trying to haul himself up, but could not, the willow was so slippery and muddy. 'Help,' he cried, 'help!' His aunt and Sally were Christians, Stephen was his friend, if they saw him they would rescue him. True, but they did not see him and he found himself being pushed back into the water by many bending branches. A green voice spoke into his ear.

'Everything has to change. Why not you? Why not now?'

Under the water the willow pushed him and, presently, let him up.

He stood swaying and trembling, turning this way and that. As a brother, a nephew, a friend he had not been of the best, but as a willow he made a fair specimen and might have enjoyed it, but that he lived in dread of being cut down.

The Marmalade Fur Coat

A LANDLADY lived by the sea and let lodgings to students. The students were allowed to live in the University for their first year, but after that they had to fend for themselves. The first to come fending was a maths student. He had a big nose and jug ears, but the landlady liked him and she was a good judge of students. She showed him the cheapest room at the top of the house. When the weather got in under the tiles it was a job to get it out again.

'Move the bed if you want to light the fire,' she warned him, 'or it catches the counterpane.'

Where to? wondered the student. When he sat up in it and stretched out his arms, he touched the walls on either side.

The second to come was a chemist, a sideways sort of girl in floaty black clothes. You'll need watching, thought the landlady. The chemist took the room next to the maths student. It was bigger and had a gas fire that meant business.

The third to come was a Dutch girl from the College of Art and Design and at the sight of her the landlady's eyes lit up, for the girl wore a marmalade fur coat that matched her eyes, her freckles and her hair.

'I need a good light, a large table, also the wardrobe must be commodious for I am studying dress design and shall be cutting out,' said the Dutch girl before she was inside the door.

So she got the best room on the first floor, though she didn't think much of it.

'Well, yes, it is not perfect, but it must do. How much please?'

The landlady's son, a burly fifteen year old with a moustache, carried a card table up to the maths student's room and squeezed it under the window and put up a shelf for his books. The chemist came out of her room and touched his arm. 'I have a bad back. Could you put a piece of plywood under my mattress, please?' So he put a piece of plywood under her mattress and she stroked his arm while he did it. Then he went down and knocked at the Dutch girl's door, but 'No,' she called. 'I need nothing.'

An ancient gas stove stood on the dark little landing

between the maths student's room and the chemist's. On it he heated his baked beans and she boiled her rice. Through the open door he saw her red lampshades and her black candles and her pictures, which disturbed him. Her gas fire was on full tilt. She must have a good grant, he thought.

They didn't see much of the dress designer, she was too toffee-nosed and talented, but sometimes she called them in.

'What do you think? Is it too long? Should it be shorter? Give me your opinions.'

The maths student thought she was the most beautiful thing he had ever seen, like a jar of marmalade with the sun shining through it. The chemist envied her the fur coat.

November came. The white seafret rolled in and covered the town. It seeped into the maths student's room and he was glad to go in and warm himself by the chemist's gas fire. December came and the cold came through the tiles and refused to go out again. He wrapped himself in his sleeping bag to work, and once, not to work, in the chemist's red and black duvet with the chemist beside him. If only it was the dress designer, he would think, and *her* marmalade hair tickling my face. How I would warm her with my love!

But the dress designer needed nobody's love. Her self-love would have fuelled a bakery.

'Paris,' she laughed. 'Finished! Rome? Tokyo? Their clothes don't move! Wait till I show my collection.'

After Christmas came the snow, jolly at first, then boring, then lethal as the white ruts froze and turned black, solid and sharp as glass. The Dutch girl wore her marmalade fur coat indoors and out.

'It is cat fur from Germany,' she said when the maths student asked. 'Many ginger toms have made it.'

'Animals should not be killed to keep rich women warm,' said the maths student, his ears blazing. 'You'd look just as beautiful in a wool coat.'

'Those cats were probably pedigree and stolen, so you are a receiver of stolen goods,' said the chemist in her whispery voice.

'I do not care,' laughed the Dutch girl. 'Probably they were killed painlessly and it would not matter if they were not. What is a cat?'

She drove her scissors through the folded cloth with a noise like a cat crunching bones and laughed at them.

Her gums were pink, her tongue was pink, her teeth very white. The chemist walked away. The maths student watched the Dutch girl crawl round her paper pattern, his convictions battling his love.

January snowed itself into February and February snowed itself blind. The chemist put on weight. It's all that rice, thought the student. But it was not all that rice, it was the oldest sum in the world, one into one makes three.

'*Me?*' he said, staring at her. 'Are you sure? We only did it once.'

He fell down the stairs in a panic to the landlady. 'I'll have to marry her,' he said miserably. 'We only did it once. It takes more than once, doesn't it, to make a baby?'

The landlady sighed. These university brains! But there, we all learn differently.

'Once can be enough,' she smiled, 'but don't you marry her. If Miss Smirk-and-Whispers says it's yours, you can be sure it isn't.'

Her son came home from school dumping his schoolbag on the table, and shaking the snow from his head.

'Our chemical young lady's in the club,' said the landlady who kept no secrets from her son. 'She's told Dave he's the father.'

How red the boy's face was! From the cold. 'Dave!' he said, staring, then turned abruptly to fetch in the coal.

'He's a good boy,' sighed the landlady. 'But I wish...'

The student put his head in his hands and groaned. Love should be simple like an equation. He'd slept with the chemist, but for warmth not love. Love wasn't what had happened.

The son came back, frowning heavily. 'What are you going to do, then, Dave?'

'Marry her, I suppose,' groaned the maths student. 'I ought to.'

'Don't you,' said the landlady. 'She can have the baby here. I won't turn her out. The father'll be someone we've never thought of.'

The son shot half a bucket of coal on the fire which drowned the conversation.

It was a vile night. The chemist, slipping down the stairs, met the Dutch girl steaming up. The marmalade fur coat was powdered with snowflakes, the marmalade hair sparkled with them. Her arms were full of irises, tulips and daffodils wrapped in white sheaths of paper.

'I have arrived! My foot is on the ladder. Two of my designs have been accepted for the Young Designers of the Year show in London. I am going to be very rich and have many lovers.'

The chemist's sideways smile slipped off her face. 'Congratulations. Will you let us see them? Could you lend me your fur coat? I've got to go to the doctor and it's a long walk.'

'No, my dear, I will not lend you my fur coat. It would be bad for your conscience and, besides, it would not suit you. The snow is beautiful. Walk briskly. You will get warm. Hey, I am giving a party tonight. Come to it. Dave is coming. He is in love with me. His eyes burn with love, his ears too. Perhaps I will let him make love to me tonight. He is longing to. Or perhaps, I will just tease him a little.'

She sailed on up the stairs and the chemist slunk past her, and went out shivering in her floaty black coat.

She did not go to the party. When she got back, she sat by her gas fire, but, very late, she slipped down to the Dutch girl's room.

'Aha, you come at last! They are all gone, but have a brandy, we left you a little.'

The dress designer waved her hand at the dressing table which was covered with bottles. She was lying on the bed with the marmalade fur coat swirled round her.

The chemist went over to the dressing table and came back with two glasses.

'Oh, one for me? Well, I am very drunk, but I can drink one more.' The dress designer's eyes focused on the curve of the little belly beside her. 'I think I have to congratulate you, too, yes? I was mean to you tonight, not lending my fur coat. I was mean to Dave too. Not one little kiss did I allow him. But, I make it up, to both of you. I give you Dave! Hey, yes? I think you need him? I make you a present of Dave!'

'Thank you,' said the chemist.

'But my fur coat you shall not have.'

'No,' said the chemist. 'You keep it.'

And they drank.

That same morning, but much later, the maths student came stumbling into the landlady's kitchen. She laughed when she saw him and moved over to the dresser.

'Here, this is my specific for hangovers. My husband swore by it. Drink it down, then go for a walk.'

The student drank it down. Then put on his duffel coat and went. He felt terrible, inside, outside, every which where. He'd loathed the party. The dress designer had been besieged by men, to none of whom could he hold a candle. I shall walk down to the sea and throw my head in. I can't think and there is a demolition squad inside it.

The beach was very strange; covered in snow. Where the waves broke on the snow, they carved a grey transparent cliff that curved inwards like another wave coming down to meet the sea. It was a white and grey world, snow, sea, shingle, cliffs, seagulls. Except, the student saw, for a blob of orange and a scratch of black.

'Hey,' he shouted, 'hey! You can't dump a cat here. Come back, come back!'

But the thin bent black figure trudged away swiftly and disappeared round a cliff, leaving only a chain of footprints leading back to the cat.

'In that case,' said the student, bending down, though his head opened and shut, 'come home with me, mog.'

The landlady liked cats. 'But you'll have to look after

her. It's unusual to have a ginger female. She's very beautiful.'

The student took the cat upstairs and on an impulse knocked at the dress designer's door. There was no answer. Sleeping it off, he thought. He knocked again later in the day. There was still no answer.

In the evening the landlady said, 'I think our young fashion lady has whirled up to London to get ready for that show she was on about. She should have told me. But the young don't think, the rich don't care and foreigners don't know, and she was all three.'

The cat settled in with the student who cut down his meagre diet to buy her fish (she refused tinned food) and a cat tray and cat litter (she refused these too).

'But it's freezing,' shivered the student letting her out of the back door. 'It's deep snow. You'll get piles, you silly mog.'

'Shut that door,' called the landlady who was ironing. 'She'll ask when she wants to come in.'

'I know someone who wants a cat,' whispered the chemist, drinking cocoa by the landlady's fire. 'I'll take her to them.'

'No,' said the maths student. 'She's been shoved out

once. I'm not shoving her out again.'

'By the way,' the landlady remembered something, 'I rang the college and they said it's quite likely she's gone up to London, though she didn't inform them. She's a law unto herself they said.'

The cat mewed at the back door.

'Wherever she is, she'll have her fur coat on,' the maths student said, letting her in, 'I bet she never takes it off.'

'She'll die if she does,' smiled the chemist.

February snowed itself out and March snowed itself in. The student grew thin and white. Fish was expensive and he ached for the dress designer. Sometimes he felt like plunging a knife into his heart to stop the pain. But the cat was a comfort. She kept him warm, she kept him company and she kept the chemist off him. In bed at night with the cat curled on his chest, looking at him over the sheet, the student unfolded his misery.

'She was above me, mog. She looked down on me. But I could have climbed up to her level. When I first saw her, so big and luscious, I just wanted to make love to her, but now I want to protect her. That's rich, isn't it? Me, protecting her.' He took his hands out of the bed to stroke the cat. It purred with a rich, deep sound. 'I bet someone's got his hands on her now and she's loving it.'

That night he dreamed his love was imprisoned. He saw her leaning from a high window calling to him. He knew she was calling his name. He could see her mouth opening and shutting, but no sound came to him.

The cold increased. The snow never stopped. Even the television got tired of it. The student's teeth ached to remember eating ice cream on the front. Everywhere above road level was vanilla, but of all the cold in the cold, cold town, the coldest cold was under the tiles of his tiny room. Chilblains plagued him. The marmalade cat began to sneeze. He wrapped her in his warmest sweater and took her to the vet, paid for an injection and tablets, queued for fish, went to the chemist's shop to buy a hot water bottle.

'Such devotion.' sneered the chemist, thickening all the time and borrowing money all round.

The cat recovered, and the student collapsed. He lay in bed sweating and scarlet trying to climb an impossible tower to rescue a girl who wept and called.

'If you make him get rid of the cat, I'll nurse him,' whispered the chemist as the landlady toiled up the stairs with barley water. 'You shouldn't be climbing these stairs with your varicose veins.'

'She won't leave his side. I don't mind coming up.' (And I don't trust you, Miss Stickyfingers.) 'You keep well clear. You're allergic to cats, remember?' said the landlady, who had trouble of her own. Her son was working all hours, paper round after school, paper round before school, weekend jobs. He never brought the coal in now.

The cat crouched on the student's bed, her great eyes fixed on him. She barely ate, she hardly slept, she never left the room. She even used her tray.

'Such devotion,' smiled the landlady, emptying it.

The student recovered. He had ten days beard on his chin and his bones stood out. He reached a wasted arm for the cat and drew her to him.

'Oh, my Marmalade Princess, what a pair of scarecrows we are. Look at you, your coat's not much cop now.'

Nor was it. It was staring and ragged as an old quilt. Her eyes were sunken, her ribcage showed, but she was over the moon with delight. She purred, she wove, she kneaded, she glowed. She licked his face.

'You almost speak,' he laughed petting her.

A letter came for the student which brought him down to the kitchen, the cat cradled in his arms.

'My gran's dead. I have to go to the funeral. Could you lend me a basket to take Princess in?'

'Oh, I wouldn't advise taking the cat. Cats panic easily and she's been so ill. Leave her with me. I'll look after her.'

The cat cried and clung to him, but he unhooked her pins and put her down. Then he gave the landlady his last fiver and set off. The chemist came into the kitchen and saw the cat.

'She's staying with me till Dave gets back,' explained the landlady. 'He's had to go north, poor lad, for his gran's funeral.'

And that'll keep *you* out of my kitchen, Miss-No-Better-Than-You-Should-Be, because you're dead scared of that cat. But the chemist was braver than the landlady thought, and kinder, for she came down that evening with a plate of plaice cooked in milk and butter.

'For Dave's cat,' she smiled. 'Only you give it to her, she won't take it from me.'

So the landlady gave it to the cat, scolding herself for

her uncharitable thoughts. But the cat wouldn't touch it and the landlady ate it herself. It was a treat, but it gave her a bad night. In fact she was sick.

'I ate it too late,' she told the chemist next morning, 'and it was too rich. Also, I'm worried about my lad. What's he doing with all the money he earns? I don't see it and he doesn't spend it on himself.'

The chemist whispered and murmured and took her plate back. She came down that evening with a tin of pilchards and a bottle of tablets for cats in poor condition. She borrowed one of the cat's saucers, opened the tin and put a pilchard on the saucer, took the backbone out and hid the tablet inside while the landlady watched.

'These pills are a trial offer. They're not on the market yet,' she explained.

'Why do you have to wear gloves?' the landlady asked her.

'My hands are sore. I've just creamed them,' answered the chemist.

The next morning she asked the landlady how the cat did. The landlady pulled a sad face. She had the cat in a basket and was rushing to the vet.

'When I went out into the yard yesterday afternoon with Madam here, there was an old one-eyed ginger tom waiting for her, so I scooped her up and rang the vet, and he said, don't give her any food tonight and bring her in tomorrow morning. So I'm off with her now for it's tomming time whatever the weather. I gave her pilchard to the ginger tom to make up for his disappointment, like.'

She opened the door and battled out. The chemist stared after her. The sky looked bleak and the town bleaker, but bleaker still was the look on the sly girl's face.

That night a black shape crept into the kitchen. The landlady heard nothing, she had taken a sleeping pill. Her son heard nothing, he was drugged with fatigue. The cat heard nothing, she was sleeping off the anaesthetic.

The snow had stopped, but a wind like a surgeon's knife sliced through the town. The student got down from his last lift and thanked the driver. The heat of the cab had sent him to sleep and the shock of the wind nearly killed him. He was still weak from 'flu and his mother had begged him to stay, but he had dreamed of his princess and the fear in her voice had terrified him. He could hear what she called now. It was his name.

'I don't know what you want most, your Dutch girl or that cat,' his mother had said, 'but since neither one of 'em's here, be off with you.'

He didn't know either. Both were mixed up in his mind, the girl who was a princess in his dreams and the cat he called Princess.

'Truth is,' he mumbled as he stumbled forward. 'I'm going dotty. I'm hollow as a tube, absolute zero, one big space.'

He flailed on. It was two miles to the landlady's house and uphill all the way. Twice his legs folded beneath him, but there is one plus to absolute zero; new knowledge can flow in. The student heard the Dutch girl calling him and knew she was dying.

He got to the top of the hill and reached the gate of the house. His hand was on it to push it open when his head snapped to the left. *Not* here, *not* here, down *there* somewhere. He began to run feebly down the road to the beach. The wind drove him against the flint wall and tried to pin him there. He fought it off and crawled on, clinging to the wall. The cries were weakening now, only faint sad mews that tore at his heart. He reached the end of the road and saw the beach, white as death under an ashen sky with a single struggling shape on it. Into the snow he plunged, up to his knees, and struggled across.

'Hang on, Princess, I'm coming, girl.'

The cat heard him and raised her head. Her eyes knew him. She made a few desperate swimming strokes, her pink mouth wide with effort. He reached her, fell on his knees and put her frozen body inside his duffel, but cold is a killer, wet is a killer, and a cold wet wind kills quickest of all. Against his heart he felt her shudder and die.

After a long time (but time had gone; the world had gone) he got up, kissed the marmalade face and laid her gently on the shining shingle and watched the small waves take her away. The water darkened and flattened the fur coat till it looked like old dark wood. Well, at least she was out of it now.

He turned round and stood, eyes squeezed shut, fists clenched in his pockets. Then the space inside him began to fill. Noises flowed in. Whether he would or no, the world came back. Seagulls flapped from the cliffs, boots crunched in the snow, the wind gentled and a sob sounded near his chest.

Two arms went round him, cold lips kissed his. He opened his eyes and saw marmalade hair and marmalade eyes wet with tears. Time vanished again. With ice-cold clarity, no, with red-hot joy, he saw that his marmalade girl was back.

'Oh, Dave, Dave,' she wept and laughed. 'it has been so horrible. I have failed so miserably.'

'Hush, hush,' he soothed, hugging her till his arms cracked. 'Don't weep. You're back. But – where's your fur coat?'

His fingers had been feeling wool, and now he saw that she had on a woollen coat with large orange and yellow, pink and brown patches appliqued on it. It went wonderfully well with her hair and her wide pink mouth.

'Behind you,' she laughed. Startled, he turned and saw the marmalade fur coat floating away on the waves like a waterlogged piece of old dark wood.

'No, no,' she cried, restraining him. 'I don't want it. I've got rid of it. Oh, Dave, you would not believe what has happened to me, you would not believe.'

'Tell me,' he said, walking her up the beach. 'I'm a mathematician, if it adds up, I'll believe.'

The sun rose, the world grew beautiful. The landlady was out in the road calling the cat desperately. When she saw them she flung her arms round them. 'You bad girl,' she scolded the dress designer, 'we've been so worried.' She hurried them into the house, asked a dozen questions, listened to none of the answers, put the fire on in the dress designer's room, made an enormous tray of food and brought it up. The maths student and the dress designer fell on the food, then fell into bed and fell fast asleep, so they never heard the shriek the chemist shrieked when she heard the dress designer was back without her fur coat.

She left the house that day and never came back. Somewhere else she bore her child, somewhere else she made her mischief. The maths student and the dress designer celebrated. So did the landlady and her son (son very glad). The dress designer went to the show and the maths student went with her. She was not a failure and the student turned out to be brilliant. He discovered equations that had never been thought of (though they had existed since time began).

Only one thing they failed at. They couldn't produce a child. Nothing wrong with the maths student. Something wrong with the dress designer. So in the end they adopted.

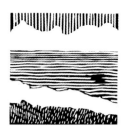

All Gone

WHAT a day it was! The last boat had left for the Caribbean carrying the last black face with it. From north to south, from east to west, look where you would, only a white face looked back at you. True, some of the white faces were browner than the black faces that had left, but they were European, which was all that mattered. Church bells pealed, fireworks exploded, bonfires blazed, whisky flowed like water. The man who had brought it about stood on a platform decorated with red, white and blue, and made a speech with the tears running down his face.

'It has been a hard fight, my friends. Two of my own lads have died in it,' his voice shook, 'but no sacrifice is too great to achieve a just end. I have never shrunk from sacrifice and, I promise you, I never will.'

'What was all that about?' twittered the sparrows on the roof of the church opposite.

'The whites have got rid of the blacks,' said the owl

who lived in the belfry. 'I saw the fighting by moonlight. The blood looked black from both sides.'

'But all humans look alike,' twittered the sparrows. 'We can't tell one from another.'

The blood was hosed from the streets, the bodies buried, the ruins rebuilt. Life began again, rather uncomfortably, there were fewer people to do the work (and much of the work was unpleasant. So many bodies to bury. So many bits of bodies) but it sorted itself. The work shrank to fit the hands to do it. The man went back to his native village. He was a simple man and his wife, who had fought alongside him, was a simple woman. His two remaining sons and his daughter returned to their own homes.

That first morning of peace, he opened his bedroom window early and looked at the white mists lying on the sleeping meadows and felt his heart swell.

'England,' he murmured, 'English, at last.'

But the peace didn't last long. Another war broke out, civil like the last, though most uncivilly waged.

'Why are they fighting now?' asked the hedge sparrows of the starlings. 'So many bombs and bullets, one daren't fly anywhere.'

'They're getting rid of the foreigners,' said the starlings, who flew everywhere. 'The Jews, the Germans, the Italians, the Greeks, the Poles, anybody who is not true-blue English. Back to the land where their great-great-great-grandparents were born, they've got to go.'

'Why?'

'Because they take the worms from the English beaks. They get up earlier.'

'Ah, well, that is a good reason,' said the hedge sparrows. 'That we can understand.'

They were perched on the lower branches of the goat willow tree, waiting for the big birds to leave the lawn.

'Well, old man,' said the woman to her husband, as they struggled into their battledress, 'here we go again.'

They locked up the cottage, a neighbour took the key. And off they went. It was a just war. They should have got rid of the foreigners when they got rid of the blacks. It was a hard war, too, but it ended at last. It cost a mint of money and a mound of bodies, but all wars do that.

On a freezing winter night, they tramped back to their cottage, got the key from the neighbour and unlocked the door. The man broke up an old kitchen chair and made a fire in the grate.

'What we've got to remember, old girl, is that we won. Hang on to that.'

She didn't answer. She was taking the photograph of their daughter out of its frame. She tore it in two and threw the pieces in the fire. The daughter had married a Dutchman, had refused to stay behind when he fled to Holland, had taken her children with her. A knock came to the door. The parish clerk stood there.

'Jim, Elsie, we know you're only just back. We know you've had a tragedy, but – but we wondered, would you come down to the village hall and give a talk to the village? Pep us up a bit? We're not – we're not downhearted, but, it's going to be a hard winter, there's shortages – '

The woman stepped forward briskly, 'Of course we'll come. Right away.' She and her husband stepped out into the bitter night and followed the parish clerk down to the unheated village hall. Both spoke simply and from their heart and the village listened.

'Fellow English men and women, let us not be sad. We have cleansed our country from all impurities. All the blood that flows in it now is English. All the brains that think in it are English. All the hearts that beat in it are English. If we cannot now make of this precious land a shining place of peace, goodness, power and wealth, it will be our fault and no one else's, but we are English and we can. It is peace now, friends, truly peace.'

'So,' said the mother housemartin to her mate next spring as they built their mud nest under the eaves of the cottage, 'why is there all this drilling and marching?'

'There's war round the edges,' her mate said. He was hanging on to the wall by tiny cracks and crevices. 'It's whispered on the wind-currents that the Welsh and the Irish and the Scots are fighting. It'll stop soon. It's only a small war.'

It didn't stop soon, but it did stop eventually.

'At last,' said the man's wife, hanging up her battledress. 'England is England and we can get on with living. Three wars is enough for me.'

All the voices on the radio and television were English. Every Celt and Gael had been driven overseas, and every Australian, Canadian, New Zealander, South African and American, for the war had rather overspread its boundaries and the original purpose had got a little muddled.

The man and his wife began setting the cottage to rights, polishing the old furniture, bringing out the family treasures long hidden in attic and cellar. They both loved beautiful things. The woman, in particular, loved flowers, and she began to remake the garden. 'I will plant only English flowers,' she said, 'and it will be a place of peace.' She made a jewel of a garden with a stone birdbath in the middle and a seat where she could sit and watch them preening and splashing.

But she found that she did not sit in her garden as much as she had hoped. There was so much to be done to get the village back to rights. There was so little petrol, food, clothes, medicines, services, so little of everything except shortages. There were plenty of those. She was so tired sometimes she fell asleep in committee.

One afternoon she carried the willow pattern teapot into the garden and sat drinking tea, watching the blue tits splashing in the birdbath. Her daughter, whom she had banished from her mind, came out from the back of her mind and sat beside her and began arguing as she used to. Her grandchildren, who had never left her heart, came out of her heart and played on the lawn. They called to her, 'Gran, Gran, watch me, watch me. Are you watching me?' She leaned forward and held out her hands to them and the empty teapot fell from her hands and rolled a little way on the grass. At sunset her husband came into the garden with a serious face and stood shaking her by the shoulder.

'He won't wake her,' said the blue tits, 'not from that sleep.'

So she never heard that a new war had started and that her last two sons were fighting in it. Protestants against Catholics was it? Or Moonies against Loonies? The owl who lived in the belfry could not explain it clearly. He only heard one side of the argument and, as he said, there must be others. Anyway, it was certainly religious, waged in the name of the God of Love by both sides and nastier than any of the others.

When it was over, all but one denomination of one religion had been vanquished and the man's family had shrunk to three, himself, a grandson and a little granddaughter. One son had turned out to be a Catholic and the other revealed that he was a Moonie. Such a falling away from the family religion shocked him deeply. Even the terrible deaths of his eldest son's family, burned alive, the youngest, escaping with the pet hamster, caught and thrown back into the flames, had not shocked him so deeply. The other son had emigrated and that, too, was treachery.

He himself had been badly wounded and was in constant pain, but he dragged himself about indomitably and taught his creed and his politics to the two who were left.

'No sacrifice is too much for one's country and the true religion. No gain without pain. Remember that.'

England seemed to have shrunk. There were markedly fewer people. Many villages and towns were deserted. Hedgerows began to sprout into woods, woods began to spread into forests. The grandson worked all hours to keep them in food from the garden. The little granddaughter worked by daylight and candlelight to keep their clothes holding together.

It was all so hard the new war made very little difference.

'The castle is in flames,' said the peacock, humbly putting his head in at the henhouse, 'may I beg the shelter of your roof for my wife and children? We have nowhere else to go.'

The hens were dubious, but they shuffled along their perches and the peacock and the peahen bowed their heads and came in and their chicks followed them.

'We haven't much in common,' the hens said amongst themselves, 'but we must be tolerant. We are all feathered.'

That was a class war and the workers won. Other wars followed. Every time a victory was won, the winning group fell into factions, the factions fought, and the stronger eliminated the weaker.

'But there'll always be differences,' one cock pheasant said to another as they stalked over the autumn fields. 'Why can't humans see that? Look at me. My ancestors have been bred so intensively that we've become melanotic. I have such bright blue feathers I'm sometimes mistaken for a peacock, while you retain the common brown plumage.'

The common brown pheasant cocked a red-rimmed eye at him and looked as though he'd like to strike his spurs through the boastful blue feathers, but refrained and they went on strutting over the sticky black furrows.

'I think it's because humans are stuck to the ground,' said the common one. 'If they could only take their feet off it and fly, they'd soon get a wider view.'

In the cottage the old man and his grandson were shouting at each other.

'Just let me *try* my ideas, that's all I'm asking, otherwise we'll bloody well *starve*.'

'Not in my lifetime, never in my lifetime. I didn't half kill myself clearing the riff-raff out of England to let foreign ways creep back.'

'You're old, Granddad, your world's gone. Those old wars you fought are history. This is the present . . .'

The old man raised his fist and struck him on the mouth. A bright line of blood flew up and the young man's hand flew to it. They glared at each other. Their eyes were exactly the same, blue and blazing, the whites suffused with blood.

'Get out!' shouted the old man. 'Get out before I kill you.'

The young man swung round, went thumping up to his room, banged about there for a few minutes, then came thundering down. His grandfather had turned his back and was standing with his fists on the mantelpiece, his head bowed between them. The little granddaughter was pressed against the wall, her sewing clutched to her, terrified.

'I'm going then, Granddad,' said the young man, hitching a bundle over his shoulder. He paused, but there was no reply. So he turned and went across to his sister.

'Leave her alone,' shouted his grandfather without turning round, 'I won't have you contaminating her.'

When the young man had gone, he went over to her, pulled her into a hard embrace, saying hoarsely, 'Don't worry, my darling, don't tremble so. We've got each other. We'll stand together.'

He stood holding her for a long time, breathing heavily, staring bulging-eyed into space while, within his arms, the child froze with fear.

Life went on, in a lame, halting, hobbling way, full of blanks, and silences, and emptinesses, and nothing much to eat or wear, although always too much to do.

One day the girl was pouring fresh water into the birdbath. A briar had grown round the birdbath and hidden beneath it, a pair of robins had built their nest in an old willow pattern teapot. The girl knew they were there, and the robins knew she knew, but neither minded the other. Her grandfather came into the garden. He looked strange, his face red and working. He came up to her, holding out his hands, whispering, 'Come, come, come, come.'

She backed away from him, but he advanced until he

laid hold of her. In a tiny voice, she said, 'Don't, don't, please don't, Grandfather, it hurts.'

'He doesn't seem very happy,' said the robins when they came next year. 'He keeps weeping.'

'It's since the girl died,' a thrush told them. 'It was his fault. She was much too young. A fledgling.'

'He quarrels with himself now,' said a blackbird, himself a quarrelsome chap. 'He's always arguing and throwing his arms about.'

'How can he quarrel with himself?' asked the hen robin.

'It's someone inside him,' answered the blackbird. 'There's two sides to the argument. If you listen you'll hear.'

The man came into the ruined garden and stood by the briar that covered the birdbath and the teapot with the robins in it. He was talking, talking, talking, taking first one side and then the other in an argument. A new self had sprung up since his granddaughter's death and he hated it. It told him things he didn't want to hear, it hinted things he couldn't believe. Worst of all, it was so un-English, it kept making him sit down and weep. He went into the house and stared into the dusty mirror over the mantelpiece, and the other self stared back at him out of his own eyes and said in his own voice, 'You were wrong. I'm telling you, you were wrong.'

The man tore at his white locks and groaned, 'You'll have to go. I won't listen to you any longer.'

He blundered about till he found a rope, stumbled up the stairs to his grandson's room and hanged himself from the beam that ran across it.

The spring went on without him. The overgrown garden burst into bloom. The birds built their nests.

'It's peaceful.' they said. 'No more wars.'

Tom Stray

ONCE there was a giant who owned a great glass tower and umpteen other blocks as well. He stood half a head higher than the tallest man on his Board (and he liked tall men on his Board) and was thick and heavy in proportion. Any man who wanted to look him in the eye had to look up to him first, and his brain was as muscular as his body and his energy was gigantic. He zapped about England making money, decisions and enemies, had no friends (didn't need any), no family (never wanted one), one sister (a dwarf).

She was tiny and had a pronounced curvature of the spine. She lived deep in the country in a cottage with two cats in a village so small it was hardly there. What she lived on the giant couldn't think. She took no favours from him. For her birthday and Christmas asked only for a tube of paint or a sable brush. Every so often, every *not* so often, he spent the night with her, more he couldn't stand. She was poor which he despised and silly which he loathed, but they had shared a terrible childhood which linked them unbreakably.

One year he went down at Christmas time thinking he might have imbibed enough goodwill to make it bearable. But at the first breakfast one of the cats, the long-haired one, upchucked on his boot (and the giant's boots were handmade).

'This bloody feline,' he swore, 'I'd boot her up the bottom if she were mine.'

'Well, she's not,' said his sister, cooking plaice for the cats at the stove. 'Take your boot off, I'll clean it. She's got fur balls. I'll brush her later.'

But the giant cleaned his own boot and while he did, the other cat, who was short-haired, whipped his breakfast bacon off his plate. The giant exploded.

'Can't these damned cats catch their own food? Countryside full of rabbits, mice –'

'It's winter. Rabbits are scarce, and the girls are getting old. But, Simpkins, that was naughty and you shall have a smack.'

She smacked Simpkins and fried the giant more bacon. He ate it, grumbling.

'Bussing to town to buy expensive fish for them. You need your head examining. I'd cut their throats. They contribute nothing.'

'We have a fish van. It calls once a week and stops outside my door, and the girls do contribute. They contribute love, and they let me love them. I need love and I need to love. I don't have the substitutes for love that you have.'

An expression came on the giant's face that would have made his Board shake, but he said nothing. His tiny sister had a way of getting deep down inside him and setting up disturbances that lasted for days.

Seeing she'd upset him, his sister, who liked to paint till the light failed, spent her day baking, while the giant strode savagely about the lanes, and when teatime came set home-made scones with fresh farm butter and home-made jam and cream, gingerbread made with black treacle, flapjacks and a little Christmas cake with the giant's own glass tower done in icing standing in the middle, before him.

'Happy Christmas, Jack,' she smiled.

The giant looked at the tea table (he hadn't sat down) so dainty, so pretty, with red-berried holly, winter flowering jasmine and a red candle in the middle and smiled a slow wide smile.

'Oh, how pretty, how very pretty, my dear. What a lot of trouble you've been to and what a pity I can't stay to enjoy it.'

And he turned and went up to his bedroom, gathered his things together and left, her disappointment music in his ears.

Back in London the pleasure of having hurt her took him happily through the accumulated mail of two days absence. Then the pleasure left him and something else took its place. Somewhere in the depth of him something was crying. The giant got angry. There's nothing I want that I haven't got; nothing I couldn't get, if I wanted it. But the crying went on, somewhere inside him.

The giant revved and roared across the land, striking bargains, smashing rivals, terrifying the government. Then one day, as he was bellowing at his Board, a pain ran up his arm, grabbed at his chest, stopped his speech and felled him to the floor.

He was rushed to hospital where pain took charge. Nothing he could do about it. Pain was master. After some weeks he came back to his handsome house and his own doctor came to see him, a man as small as the giant was big.

'You must rest,' said the doctor in his small voice.

The giant thrust out his thick lips. 'I either sleep or wake. If I wake, I work. I don't know how to rest.'

This was true. It was an odd area of ignorance in a man who knew so much.

'The equation's very simple,' said the doctor who had more courage than body. 'If you rest, you live, if you don't, you –'

His little hands fluttered for a moment, then dropped.

Die, thought the giant. *Die*, me?

He lay and gloomed. Death did not scare him, but – not doing? He couldn't imagine it. If I'm not – doing, then – I'm not. I'm nothing. He rang his sister.

'I'm to do nothing,' he tried to bellow, but his voice only scratched the air.

'Then come here,' she answered. 'We're famous for nothing.'

His manservant packed his cases, his chauffeur drove him down. Just getting into his car, just sitting in it, and then, just getting out of it again, tired him unbelievably. He stumped past his sister's welcome and lowered himself into her one reasonably sized armchair. He'd always found it a tight fit, now it was spacious. She brought him tea and put it at his elbow. He drank a cup, ate a slice of bread and butter, and found that enough. There was a soft flump. The long-haired cat had landed on his knees. He raised his hand to knock it off, but his hand just brushed along its fur. Like silk. The fur was like silk. Like the softest silk.

He was amazed, and began to stroke it. Ripples of pleasure, of soothing pleasure, travelled up his fingers to his brain, and this, too, amazed him. The pleasure was mutual. The cat purred and kneaded.

'Take your pins out, girl, and settle down,' he commanded in a scratchy whisper. 'You're hurting.'

Calling it *girl*! Talking about pins, admitting to hurt! I'm going soft. He saw cream buns. They floated before him, pale and brown, cream bulging from their middles. Where and when had he ever had cream buns? He lay back, his big hand resting on the silky fur. He was very fond of silk. Had a silk dressing-gown, silk pyjamas, liked to dress his mistresses in silk. Now I've got a silky cat. Fatigue closed his eyes and he slept.

After that the long-haired cat often leapt on his lap. Preferred him to her basket. 'She'll leave hairs on you,' warned his sister and offered him a teatowel to put over his knees. He waved it away, though he was a meticulous dresser.

The long-haired cat was meticulous, too. She washed and washed.

'Her shirtfront's whiter than a head waiter's,' said the giant, and noticed other things about her. Her deftness, her gracefulness, the way she had of putting her head on one side and gazing up at him adoringly. Her purr was a song of love.

'Beautiful, yes,' agreed his sister, 'but stupid. She can't do any of the things her sister can.'

'Doesn't need to,' retorted the giant. 'She can get herself loved. That's clever enough. Get yourself loved and you can get anything you want.'

Something I've never done. But I didn't need to. But, when strength goes, power goes. How d'ye get what you want then?

The weather went silly, primroses came out, violets bloomed, pinks and pansies opened taking no notice of the calendar. The giant took a stick and went walking with his silky girl, but she would only go half-way down the lane one way and half-way down the lane the other way. Never any further.

'Ah,' said the giant, understanding, 'your patch, eh? Well, I have a patch too, and I patrol it.'

Because he walked slowly now, and had to stop and lean on his stick, he noticed things. Batty blue cornflowers blooming in the warm moist air and a poppy, a lunatic poppy, floating its scarlet petals against the January sky.

'Flowers?' mused the giant. 'A garden, hey?'

Foolish flowers. Improvident gamblers with no resources. In a night the mild weather vanished and the cold rolled in, snow, snow and more snow. The village was cut off, the cottage marooned. Snow filled the lane from hedgetop to hedgetop. A farmer came on a tractor to take his sister shopping. While she was gone a crying came at the back door. The giant opened it and a black cat shot in and laid its jaws to the cats' saucers.

'Hey, out, out, that's not yours,' cried the giant and booted it out, but it whipped round and forced its way in again. This time the giant gave it a boot on the nose that sent it flying, and slammed the door.

Cream buns again and this time himself with them! A great, raw-boned lad in a baker's shop pinching half price stale buns. Well, I hadn't got half the price, not even half the half price. The baker's wife came into the shop from the back with a kitten in her hand, a pale brown little thing with a fat little tum. 'We call him Cream Bun,' she said smiling. 'He's exactly like one. Stroke him.' I put the tip of my finger, my great red finger, on its head, practically covered it. And felt silk! Silk! It was hard as a nut and silky. 'Here,' she said, 'those stale things won't fill you, take some cream buns. Quickly, before my husband comes. Take four, I'll put the money in the till.' A red letter day. I've never forgotten it. Well I have, I did, till today.

'Yes, I know that cat,' his sister said when she returned and he told her. 'He's a stray. He's very friendly. He goes all around the village trying to fit himself in.'

'Why don't you take him in? You love cats.'

'The girls wouldn't accept him.'

'Couldn't he live outside?'

'Well, yes, he could.'

So the giant went outside and made a shelter for the stray. I *am* going soft. He caught sight of it bucking across the snow covered field beyond the garden, sinking to its nose tip at every plunge. Again his hungry youth came back to him so vividly his belly griped. And the cold! The chilblains I had! Dreadful broken ones on my ears.

His sister came down the path, scarved and shawled,

carrying an armful of jumpers. I must clear that path or she'll fall and break a hip.

'Put these in his box, they'll keep him warm, they're only jumble. I've put flea powder on them, which will help him.'

The black cat was back next day, begging and pleading. They enticed him down to his new home with a saucer of cat food. He crouched to eat it, ears back, looking all the time for a boot. A piece of skin was missing from his nose and the wound was red and raw. The giant winced when he saw it, knowing how that would sting and that he was responsible.

'Now he's had a meal and is comfortable, if you hold him I'll do his eyes, they look awful,' said his tiny sister. 'Hold him in this.' She gave him a thick towel.

He wrapped the cat in it and held him while his sister gently wiped away the discharge. He was astonished at her lack of squeamishness.

'But once the snow goes,' she said, 'I'll have to get the murder van. It's a shame, but the girls will gang up on him in the garden.'

'The murder van?'

'The R.S.P.C.A. They'll take him away and put him

down. They'll try to home him, but nobody takes a tom.'

'Can't he live off the land – when spring comes?'

'Not round here. The farmers use pesticides and put down poison. Rabbits have almost been wiped out. Anyway, I'm not going to add to the population of feral cats. But we'll feed him up, give him a brief spell of good living. I'd like him to know love.'

The sunsets were wonderful that last week in January, like tremendous stories. The giant would sit stroking the long-haired cat, watching the colours battling it out until one clear colour was left with a single star hanging like hope.

'I suppose we have sunsets in London?' he asked his sister.

'You've blocked them out,' she answered. She was drawing him. He looked at her pencil. 'Draw me the cat,' he ordered. So she took a fresh sheet and drew the long-haired cat singing its love for him. 'No, not this soft thing, Tom Stray yonder.' So she took another sheet and drew the stray ranging blackly over the snow.

February came. Primulas reappeared from under the vanishing snow looking as though they'd had a bath. The giant's sister got out the telephone directory.

'Don't send for the murder van, Lettie. I'll pay for his keep.'

'It's not a question of money. The girls would give him hell.'

The voice that answered her query shook. 'Do you know many cats I have collected and put down since Christmas? Over three hundred healthy animals! What do you think that does to an animal lover?'

'I'm so sorry, I'm so sorry.' The giant's sister put the phone down and ruminated. 'I could try the Cats Protection League, or Animal Shelter, or there's Animal Rescue; though probably they're overbooked, too, and I know they're underfunded, because I contribute to them. I doubt there's a cats' home will take him, even if we had him neutered.'

The giant's big hand reached out and took the phone from her and crashed it down.

'Then by the Lord, I'll build my own,' he swore.

He sent for his manservant and chauffeur and boarded them in the village. He hired a secretary and started in, dictating from his chair with the long-haired cat on his knee, or walking up and down with her clinging to his chest, singing her song of love. Land was bought, architects hired, leading veterinarians consulted, every likely source of income bombarded.

The giant's big frame quivered, his eyes brightened, his voice took on a deeper note. He was alive again, *his* sort of aliveness. True, he had only half his strength, but half his strength was enough for this. Nothing could stand against him, only his sister, and she was with him and where his bludgeoning bellow failed, her flickering words won.

By late summer Cats' Cradle was rising from the ground. By the following spring it was finished. It was like no other cats' home in the world.

It was laid out in gardens and buildings, more gardens and more buildings: luxurious rooms (you couldn't call them cages) for top people's cats, costing the earth to hire (but not to run); a restaurant with marvellous food at marvellous prices; a gallery for exhibitions, a theatre, just about everything that would draw people and make money, and at the back, away from all the razzmatazz, Mogtown, with cages for ordinary cats at ordinary prices and for strays at no prices, a hospital for sick cats, etcetera, etcetera.

The giant hired experts to run the different parts and the experts hired their own staff. With his tame accountant and bullied bank manager he funded the whole complex with the skill and deviousness that had built his empire.

Exactly a year from the day that he had reached for the telephone, the opening took place with Tom Stray himself making a guest appearance, sleek and satin coated, and unneutered.

Before the giant paid the architect off, he got him to design a house near Cats' Cradle and his sister, and there he took Tom Stray to live.

'No dogs,' he grinned when a reporter asked. 'I've got my own pack up in town.'

He commissioned a young student, a girl, to design the garden and he began to collect pictures, Victorian ones that told a story and moderns that jangled with colour and told no story.

'What do you think of our chairman's taste in art?' inquired one Board member of another after a visit. 'Bit bruising, what?'

'Oh, I don't know,' replied the other. 'I rather get a lift from colour.'

Other charities came queuing at his door, but the giant pushed out his thick lips at them. 'Humans can look after themselves. Or if they can't, their governments can, or if they can't their neighbours can. There's not a country on this earth that hasn't got money about it somewhere. Go and dig it out.'

Tom Stray lived much like the giant, master of a huge territory and sometimes away for days. When he came back the giant would talk to him.

'My Board's trying to get rid of me, Tom, if only they knew! My mini sister will live to be a hundred.' (She did in fact live to her late nineties, a famous painter of flowers.) 'But I've such a pain here, Tom,' touching his chest, 'but I can't rest. Never learned how.'

He tried to stroke Tom Stray down on to his lap, but Tom Stray leapt down and took himself off to the kitchen.

Another January came, splendid with sunsets. The giant who had been huffing and puffing up to London, flattening the Board, went suddenly weak and breathless. He was driven down to his country house and sat propped up in his huge bed, which he'd had raised up on a platform so that he could see his garden. I've finished with the Board, finished with that London house, almost finished with this great hulk of a body, but what comes next? No harps and angels, but surely something? Since I can't do, I'll go, but I'd like to go easy and now here's a surprise, he smiled at himself, never thought I'd think this, I should like to go with someone! He thought over his life, his business associates, his mistresses, his fellow tycoons, but none of those fitted. I've finished with them.

A sunset came of great beauty and movement. 'Leave it, leave it,' he whispered as his manservant moved to draw the curtains. His eyes stared at the colours battling it out over the wood where Tom Stray was hunting. The wood was the giant's and rabbits were allowed. A letter lay under the giant's left hand.

His sister wrote she was sorry he was ill and she'd be coming to see him. 'But your silky girl is very frail and I don't like to leave her. She stays in her basket all day, nothing left of her really, except her purr, and her love. She's seventeen. A good age for a cat, though not the greatest.'

The diminutive doctor slipped into the room. The secretary had sent for him. Then the nurse, and the chauffeur.

The giant's head turned on the pillow. His thick lips mouthed, 'Get – out.' Not you, his eyes said to the doctor, then turned back to the window.

A magical clear green with one small star hung above the wood, which was now jet black, all detail lost.

The chauffeur, the nurse and the manservant left the room. The doctor stayed in the shadows watching. A sound began in the room which the doctor recognised but could not believe. He began to walk softly about, looking. The giant's stare left the window and his eyelids slowly lowered. His right hand lifted and began a rhythmic curving movement a few inches above the bedclothes that covered his chest. Then the sound that couldn't be there and the movement of the right hand stopped and the doctor saw that the giant had gone easy and (though this he didn't see) accompanied.

The Three Candles

I T was the morning of Christmas Eve, so dark the street lamps were still on. Snow was falling, covering the trodden snow of yesterday and the tramp asleep on the bench.

Three stories up Carrie Oling's bony toes found first the carpet, then her slippers. *Come on, Carrie, up, up, up!* Her mother's voice, silent in the grave these many years, but not silent in Carrie. No lie-ins had ever been allowed, not even on Boxing Day when all the work was done. All right, Mum, I'm up, Carrie answered her mother in her mind as she went across to the window to peer between the curtains.

Snow! Oh, thank you, God! *Snow*, Your free gift of beauty. Pure magic. Childhood came flooding back. Except that childhood had not been pure magic. Mother had not allowed magic. Bare feet on freezing linoleum. Waking hungry, going hungry. But that's a long way behind me now, Carrie comforted herself, enjoy the snow, *enjoy*. Thirty-eight years ago, she'd been born in the Poor Row. Now she lived in William Square, Number Three, rich Miss Carrie Oling.

Get on, Carrie! There's work to be done before the setting of the sun. Oh Mother! You never let any of us stand and *be*, except in church. Always scolding, never pleased. But the snow was soothing her. Her eyes grew dreamy watching the falling flakes, and that girl's voice she'd heard last night as she was falling asleep came back, and snow and song wove a magic that made her sway with pleasure.

Oh, come on, come on, come on, run the bath, make the bed, get dressed, start the day, no time for dreaming, so much to do —

Her mother's voice or hers? Couldn't tell. Mother was always inside her. But she must get on, she must or the pit of blackness would open and she would fall in, blackness close over her, cold kill her. She was always skating over a pit of blackness. If you kept moving, kept doing, kept very, very busy, it didn't open, but you mustn't stop, you mustn't ever stop.

She flung her clothes on, didn't wash (how shocked Mother would have been) ran down the stairs and across the street to the tramp.

The tramp was standing up, shaking herself about. It

was a woman tramp, tall, broad, in a thick coat and a broad-brimmed hat. A hard, flat face, black eyes. Strength and power. Carrie opened her purse.

'C-can I help you? Offer – offer a cup of tea, a hot breakfast? Some money to – to buy food?'

Strong white teeth in a wide smile, good-humoured creases around the eyes, a broad palm held out.

'A gold coin and a silver and I tell your fortune, lady.'

'I – I don't want my fortune told, I – I don't believe in fortune telling,' Carrie looked up. How tall the tramp was! Taller than Carrie and Carrie was tall. 'Here's a pound coin for gold and a five pence for silver, I'm sorry I haven't got a ten or a twenty. But, please, let me give you something hot. I could bring it across.'

The tramp took the money and slipped it into a pocket, then she heaved the sack her head had been resting on off the bench, opened the neck, plunged her arm in, and brought out a little carved wooden Christmas tree. Very old and rather battered, but the paint still showing its colours. There were three candles on its branches, one on the lowest branch, one in the middle and one on the top. She held the tree out to Carrie.

'Light each candle with a good deed and the last wish

you wish before the stroke of midnight will come true.'

'N – no, no, oh no,' stuttered Carrie. She always said no to presents, to any offer of kindness. It was almost impossible to give Carrie anything. 'No, please, not to me. I'm a social worker, I – I do good deeds all the time, professionally. It wouldn't be fair. G – give it to someone else, please.'

Amusement on the strong face. 'You've taken it, lady.'

A yelp from Carrie, who saw she had.

The tramp swung the sack up over her shoulder and strode off. Carrie stood holding the little tree, shaking violently.

Well, of *course* (her mother's voice) you silly child, it's *snowing*. Get inside before you catch your death.

But Carrie stood, the tree in one hand, her purse in the other, teeth chattering, thoughts flying this way and that. Oh, oh, the black pit was opening, cold –

But – *my hand's warm*! The only bit of me that is. The rest of me's freezing, but my hand's warm. The hand holding the tree. It was true.

It wasn't imagination. But –

Get indoors! Or the black pit will open! Her mother's voice, sharp as an east wind. Cold will cleave you, darkness drown you.

But for once the black pit didn't galvanise Carrie. She stood looking up the street. The tramp had vanished. Snow had closed her footprints. Snow was covering the bench. Snow is covering me, thought Carrie, but not the tree. A snowflake touched the tree and vanished, like a kiss that brushes a cheek and is gone. *Oh, Carrie* (her mother's weary sigh) *you dreamy child.*

She turned and hurried across to her house, up the posh steps, in the handsome door, put the tree on the hall table, ran up the stairs, flung off her snowy coat, her clothes and, soon, lay in a scented bath, smiling blissfully.

'Mother,' she said aloud. 'The black pit hasn't opened!' And she lay in the hot water and let snow and song and storybook magic fill her mind.

She came down to breakfast. Claire, her little lame duck, was sitting at the table slitting the mail. Requests for money, appeals from charities, agendas for AGMs, rotas for helping at The Shelter for January, February, March, invitations to charity balls, charity this, charity that, charity the other. Nothing real. It *is* real, cried Carrie, shocked at herself. It's my life! She blinked and noticed Claire.

Luminous as a star. Shining, glowing, her little face alight.

'Claire! You look – you look –' What did Claire look?

Beautiful? No, no, Claire was plain, her little plain duck. She looked – enchanted. 'Claire, do you believe in magic?'

'Oh, yes!' A long ecstatic sigh, her little face rose pink.

'Let's put it to the test!'

She told Claire about the tramp and the tree. 'Run and find some matches and let's see if we can light the first candle.'

Claire ran, she hadn't touched her breakfast, came back with the matches, panting.

'Right, but first the good deed!' Carrie reached for the telephone, always one near her and dialled.

'Warden, please. Paul? That you? Paul, listen, yes, I know it's early, but I've had a splendid idea. I'm going to take over the whole of tomorrow's rota at The Shelter. Yes, yes, I know, I know Jean and Phyllis are doing it, but they've both got families, I haven't, I've nothing special on, and I want to do it. You've got a family, too, so go to it! Don't thank me, don't, I'm not good samaritaning, I want to.'

She put the phone down; Claire was gazing at her with awe.

'Now, then, give me the matches. We'll start at the bottom candle and work our way up.'

She marched out to the hall, Claire following, and stood before the little tree. 'Magic, Claire! Watch.'

She struck a match and held it to the bottom candle, and held it till the flame nearly burnt her finger and thumb, then blew it out and dropped it. 'Well, what an obdurate candle!'

They went back to the dining room. 'My cheque book,' commanded Carrie. Claire ran, and came back with the cheque book.

'There!' smiled Carrie, her pen flying furiously, 'That's for the mad woman on the heath. That'll stop the Council closing her down.'

The mad woman on the heath was a sort of saint who rescued dumped and straying animals, fed them, nursed them, kept them, wouldn't part with them.

There were frequent agitations against her.

'Now then, we'll try again, but post the cheque.

Post it first!'

Claire took the envelope and ran, out to the pillar box at the corner of the square, and back, flushed and laughing, snowflakes sparkling on her.

Carrie struck a match and held it to the bottom candle. It wouldn't light, wouldn't even smoulder, wouldn't acknowledge the flame at all.

'The wick's damp, of course.' said Carrie, but it wasn't and she knew it wasn't. 'Ha, *I* know.'

I sound like my father, always rising to a challenge, always rolling up his sleeves and squaring up to life.

'My writing paper, Claire, quick.'

Claire ran, was back in a flash with Carrie's embossed writing paper, her stamped leather blotter, and her gold fountain pen.

Carrie pulled up a chair to the hall table and dashed off a letter scored with underlinings, bristling with exclamation marks. 'There! Put that in the post! It's an invitation for my demon aunt to come and stay! For a week! I've said I'll send the car for her!'

Claire gasped. She'd met the demon aunt. A deeply carven, deeply unlovable standing stone of rectitude. No mellowing moss had ever gathered itself to her, though she had rolled nowhere, rollicked never, no spark of love ever struck from her flinty heart.

'That should set the tree on fire! Run, Claire!'

Claire ran, posted, sped back, face bright as a holly berry.

'Hurray! At last my demon aunt will have a flame!' Carrie laughed as she made the joke, struck a match and held it to the bottom candle. 'I can't *believe* it! I *cannot believe* this.'

For the wick would not light, not light at all.

'Oh Claire, what nonsense this is! What are we doing here, playing games like children? Wasting good working time, believing *nonsense*.'

She blew out the match and turned away.

'Put the tree in the jumble sack in the cloakroom.'

'Oh no, let it stay,' Claire pleaded. 'Let it be part of Christmas. I'll put some holly round it.'

Carrie looked down at her. Her little lame duck. Her ill temper vanished. 'All right. You cosset it. I'm sorry, Claire, that tramp had me believing! Are you very disappointed?'

Claire shook her head. 'No, I don't think magic's meant to be easy.'

Easy! Spending the whole of Christmas Day at The Shelter, giving a thousand pounds to a batty old woman for her unwanted animals, inviting an unpleasant old lady to stay for a *week*, easy? *Easy?*

Claire was speaking. 'The letter to your aunt, the cheque to the animal woman, shall I ring the bank, tell them to stop the cheque? Say you've been called away, that you can't –'

'No, no, the letters have gone. They'll do no good, but they've gone. I shan't miss the money and my aunt would never have come. She wouldn't come if you sent a coach and horses for her. She won't leave her own house. Grumbles all the time that no-one invites her, but won't go if they do. Let's get working.'

She spoke wearily. She felt – well, what did she feel? She watched Claire return to the dining room and come out again with her arms full of mail, letters, catalogues, reports, papers. How gracefully she moved, like a ballerina, a ballerina taking a curtain call, arms full of roses, lilies, carnations. *Carrie!* Mother's voice, *stop romancing, work.*

'What do you know about magic, Claire?'

A lovely smile, a ballerina smile. 'It's unexpected.'

The morning took on a disgruntled, lumpy feeling like a bad mattress. Carrie couldn't get comfortable with it. At work all was jollity and letting go, goodwill beamed from every face, well, not every one.

Her boss said, 'Carrie! Are you all right? You look so sad. It's Christmas tomorrow. You adore Christmas!'

She tried to lift herself, but could not. She was outside the glow and sparkle and could not get in. When at the end of the day a young woman with a square sulky face walked into her office and flumped down saying, 'I've walked out, left 'em an' I'm not going back. 'E can cook the turkey, get the flaming pudding out, take the kids to fetch 'is Ma, dish out, make the gravy, and wash up and get the tea and take 'is Ma back and get the kids to bed and if 'e's sane at the end of it, I 'ope it's a Christmas 'e'll never forget.'

Carrie was glad. This was something she could get into. She was a good listener, a good rememberer, a clear thinker, but instead of saying, 'Tell me' and listening quietly, she leaned forward and said urgently, 'But you must go back, you must, or you'll lose Christmas! You mustn't lose this Christmas, you mustn't!'

The sulky face looked astonished, the lips parted,

the eyes widened; a great improvement on the scowl and the pushed-out lower lip.

'What's so great about this Christmas? You tell me.'

'It's our one chance of magic! It may not be religious, but it *must* be magic. It's the only time we have magic, Christmas, and when it snows.'

The young woman was staring at her, and sitting up straighter.

Carrie went on, 'You must be there. You make it happen. Christmas is a parcel of lovely, shining things, love, presents, special food, firelight, candles, children, giving. You're the one who makes the parcel, who unwraps it, gives –'

She stopped, feeling quite desperate. The young woman was heaving herself up. 'You got a partner? Kids? A ma-in-law? No? Didn't think you had.'

She went out. Carrie ran round her desk to the door and into the corridor, calling after her, 'Where are you going?'

The young woman marched on, with a flick of her head. 'See if the turkey's alright.'

Doubt attacked Carrie. Did I do right? The young husband might have enjoyed wrestling with the turkey, making the gravy, no, he wouldn't enjoy that, gravy's tricky, but his mother would have helped. It might have been nice for her, being mother and son again, and then when the girl came back, as she would, there'd be hugs and kisses. The young man would have learned something and so might she. I got it wrong, I'm sure I got it wrong.

The Fecklesses. *Carrie* her mother said, urgent inside her, *what's done is done*. The Fecklesses.

Carrie brightened. The Fecklesses, her favourite failing family, hopeless, but gorgeous. She drove to them gladly and staggered into their crowded living room (never was a room so aptly named, the amount of living that was done in it) smiling in anticipation and the Fecklesses rose as one with cries of joy.

'There,' smiled Carrie, unpacking her baskets. 'As per usual, one Christmas pudding, one Christmas cake, and a dozen mince pies, made by me for you with my best wishes!'

But, 'No, no,' cried the Fecklesses, beaming like lighthouses, 'put them back. We've made *you* a cake this Christmas!'

And they piled her gifts back in the basket, pushed her lovingly into a chair, pulled an enormous lopsided

Christmas cake towards her with a grubby grey snowman, a battered Father Christmas and an Eskimo sinking to their waists in unset icing.

'Our Maureen made it! Stayed up late last night to finish the icing, though she'd such a cold, her nose was dripping so she could hardly get her handkerchief to it in time. But when she got that job at the hospital you got her, she said, this Christmas we're going to give Miss Oling a cake and *I'm* going to make it!'

'And,' cried sister Raylene, 'there's another treat! I got two bottles of best British sherry-type wine to drink with it!'

Caught in the jaws of love, an enormous wedge of cake on a red paper plate in her lap, a glass of sherry-type British wine balancing on the arm of her chair, Fecklesses radiating warmth all around her like a circle of electric fires, Carrie found that the words *No thank you* would not pass her lips. So she put the thin end of the wedge to them instead and took a bite. Forgive me, she begged her stomach, do your best.

It was the heaviest cake she'd ever eaten and the sherry was like cough mixture, but all mouths were full and conversation impossible, so no lies were needed.

(*Lies are never needed*, her mother again, though Carrie often found they were.) She beamed and nodded, gave the thumbs up, and the Fecklesses did likewise.

'Another slice for Miss Oling, Raylene, and give her a top up, her glass's half empty!'

'Oh, call me Carrie, please! After all these years!' She managed to mumble through an acre of cake.

She finished the king-sized slice. (How much had it weighed?) She wrapped the second in a red paper serviette and took her leave, ribs crushed by Feckless' hugs, stomach in shock, palate affronted. Bed, she thought, tablets, lie down, drink lots of water, I must not have a migraine. There's still the shopping.

But as she turned into William Square, she saw Claire by the gate cutting the holly, which this year was loaded with berries, and giving it to the most outlandish of the young men next door, the one with the green hair and a ring through his left eyebrow. He went off, holly sprouting from his arms, looking like a tree god.

'Oh, Carrie,' Claire began before Carrie could speak. 'Paul rang. He said Phyllis and Jean say thank you very, very much, but they want to do The Shelter tomorrow. They've made a programme of games and music, their families are coming to help and they are all looking forward to it so, Paul says, please *don't* come! And, oh, Carrie, we're asked to a party tonight next door!'

'Next door?'

'Yes, the Overdrafts.'

'Oh, the young men, the band.'

Last thing I want to do, absolutely the last thing. She opened her mouth to say no, but Claire was running up the steps and disappearing through the door, which she'd left open while cutting holly. All my expensive central heating wasted on the front garden and all my lovely holly gone next door!

Putting the holly up on Christmas Eve is the best part of Christmas, because Christmas Eve *is* magic, it doesn't have to try. Whereas Christmas Day turns into indigestion, headaches and loneliness, for wherever you spend it, abroad, with friends or relations, you're always on the outside.

'How do you like her? Isn't she beautiful?'

One of the young men was calling.

She turned. 'Oh!'

They'd built a snowman, no, no, a snow *woman*, a huge one. (*Disgusting, no need, never any need to emphasise sex*! Mother, of course.) The young men had felt a need, my word, they had.

'She's Mother Christmas!'

'I'd sooner she was clothed.'

'Why? Snowmen only wear hats and scarves.'

'She's – very big.'

'Big is beautiful.'

Carrie, who was herself that way, paused. Mother had been little and skinny but me, I'm father's side, built like a barn door.

'I think you'll find the Square won't like her.'

'Why not? Snow is beautiful. Mothers are marvellous. Bodies are what we live in. Thank you for the holly. We couldn't afford any, and when we could the shops had sold out.'

Carrie's heart melted.

'Coming to our party?'

Not on your life, thought Carrie. 'Yes,' she said.

'Great! See you then.' With a wave of his hand he was gone.

I am my own worst enemy. She climbed the steps wearily and saw that the bottom candle on the little tree had been lit.

'Claire, Claire!!' she called, forgetting to shut the door.

No answer. She walked into the dining room, the morning room and the room they used as an office. Claire was not there, but upstairs in the drawing room, she found her, waltzing dreamily round the room, hands crossed on her breast. She hadn't drawn the curtains and Carrie could see the Christmas lights twinkling in the trees in the square, and little cameos of busy people putting up decorations in their rooms, holly behind pictures.

'Claire, you sweet thing, did you light the candle? To give me a little magic?'

'Candle?' Carrie could have said elephants.

'*Candle*. On the little Christmas tree. In the hall. The bottom candle. Oh, Claire, do stop waltzing and listen.'

Claire stopped. 'Tree? Oh, the tree. Is the candle lit?'

'Yes. Has anyone been in?'

'No. Only me, except when I was delivering cards round the Square and when I was cutting holly, and when I was delivering cards I locked the front door. The Square's *so* friendly, I had sherry and mince pies at nearly every house.'

'Did you take a card to the boys next door?'

'Oh, yes, they were terribly impressed. It's the grandest they've ever had.'

(*Don't forget the young men, Carrie, it may bring them to God.*)

Well, if they've got the card, at least they know I'm not being toffee-nosed. I won't go to the party, but shop I must. Aloud, she said, 'Well it's a mystery, but right now I must get to the shops, though I'm dead beat – '

She waited for Claire to say, 'No, no, don't! Have a rest. I'll go. I'd love to.' And other lame duck things. But Claire didn't. She was waltzing again, this time with her eyes closed. A spurt of anger made Carrie hot. I rescued her. I gave her a home and a job. I pay her. The *least* she could do – no, no, no, don't go down that road. She's young, it's Christmas Eve, there are young men next door and a party to go to. You go shopping, you old warhorse.

Trying hard to oust self-pity, never an easy lodger to evict, Carrie dumped her basket of unwanted cake, pudding and pies, seized a shopping bag covered with Monet's waterlilies, bought at the Royal Academy's last exhibition, and made for the front door. There was a little street of specialist shops, one of which sold wonderful food, treats, costing the earth, from all corners of the earth, a few minutes from William Square. She flung open the front door and – Mrs Drear!

Oh, no, not Mrs Drear! But, oh yes, Carrie, did you think that Fate had finished with you? She had Mrs Drear up her sleeve. Christmas is a time of goodwill and what is goodwill unless tested to the utmost?

'Mrs Drear!'

'Oh, Carrie, I did call, but you were out. I just want to wish you a happy Christmas.'

'Well, come in and wish me a happy Christmas by the fire.'

For Mrs Drear was a notorious not-coming-inner, a hoverer on doorsteps, a lingerer at gates. Thousands of pounds of expensive hot air had flowed from front doors while Mrs Drear didn't come in. Carrie's mind raced. The shops stay open late. I'll give her half an hour, then leave her with sherry and nibbles. If I offer them now, it'll only prolong the agony.

Keeping her coat on as a hint (new this winter, wonderful wool, Norwegian mountain sheep, wonderful red dye glowing like a flame) Carrie seated Mrs Drear by the fire in the morning room and, sitting opposite her, fixed a bright interested gaze on her face, and Mrs Drear began.

She's unique, thought Carrie, as Mrs Drear's flat monotone drifted past her ears wavering a little up, a little down. Other bores work up to it, but she bores from the beginning. Quite an art. If it could be piped, if her boringness could be canned, bottled, *used* for something, what a fortune she'd make. It could be used instead of anaesthetic. Or piped into people's houses to be switched on when they couldn't sleep.

'... and I thought he was just sleeping and I thought oh good because he'd had such bad nights and I got up and made myself tea and then I got up and made myself breakfast and then I got worried because he felt cold so I made two hot water bottles and got back into bed and lay beside him then I had to get up because it was Christmas Eve and there were things to do and later when I went up to look at him he was still sleeping and his head was so cold so I put an eiderdown over him and got in under it and thought I'll warm you love and I fell asleep and when I woke he was just the same and didn't stir so I rang the doctor who wasn't best pleased because it was Christmas Eve but he came and said your husband's dead Mrs Drear he's been dead for hours and it was such a shock I felt so stupid because –'

'*Dead*!' cried Carrie, and suddenly she was there, in the bedroom. 'That was awful, *awful*!'

'Yes, it was,' quavered Mrs Drear, 'that's why I keep talking about it. I can't ever get it out of my mind.'

'It was *brutal* of the doctor! He should *never* have told you like that.'

'He was busy, Carrie, he wanted to get on. It was Christmas Eve, I should have noticed – '

'Go on,' commanded Carrie fiercely. 'Go on. Tell me everything.'

The black pit had opened, cold and deathly. You thought you were doing the right thing and all the time you were clasping a corpse and everyone knew but you.

So Mrs Drear went on and Carrie listened with every cell in her body. Two hours later she saw Mrs Drear out and stood on the top step with the front door wide open while Mrs Drear thanked her again and again and again and again.

'No one's ever listened as you did, Carrie. I feel so much better. I even feel lighter.'

Of course you do, thought Carrie as she smiled and

waved, all your drear's inside me now. She watched Mrs Drear walk off with a brisker step and a straighter back and thought, so that's listening. All the times I thought I was doing it, I wasn't. I was just waiting to get in and spout myself.

She turned and went in, saw that the second candle was alight and smiled sadly, remorseful that she had never listened until now and sad that Claire should have to play at magic.

Where was Claire? Well, somewhere obviously, and working. She was a conscientious child.

What now? Shopping? No, no. She was too heavy with Mrs Drear's sadness. Bed, a sleep before that dreadful party.

She hauled herself up the stairs to her bedroom, pulled the duvet over her and sank immediately into a black and white dream so cold it froze her. Black vaulting sky, black sea, no stars, no moon, no reflections. The black pit! Cold cleaving her, darkness drowning — but, she was not drowning! I am just here, just here in it and it's quite jolly. There was an iceberg crowded with polar bear cubs, another with penguins, one had a girl on it with her legs dangling over. Her iceberg drifted over to Carrie, who found that *she* was on an iceberg too. The girl was paper thin and dead white. Like a cut-out, thought Carrie. The girl said crossly, 'Stop batting me down. You're always batting me down.'

Carrie was shocked. 'I don't bat you down. I wouldn't bat you down. Mother was always batting *me* down.'

'You *do*, all the time, you never stop. I'd like a happy Christmas, too, you know.'

Her iceberg drifted away. Carrie tried to follow, but could not. The black space widened and widened. The cold increased.

She woke. The duvet had slipped off, and she was freezing. 'I forgot to close the window!'

The young men's music was thumping in her ears and the girl was singing. That song! It breaks my heart. The song and the iceberg girl's sullen face joined Mrs Drear's sadness and spread through her. No, no! Carrie jumped up. I won't be drowned, I won't. She hauled a dress out of her wardrobe, leapt under the shower, dressed, made up and ran downstairs. Pulled on her glowing red coat ('it's like a hug from a friend') and, on an afterthought, ran down into the kitchen and seized the basket with her rejected cake and pudding. 'You *shall* have a home,' she told them. 'You *shall* be loved.'

She went out and in at next door's gate. Mother Christmas, she noticed, was wearing a crown of holly. Through the open front door and the empty hall and up the uncarpeted stairs went Carrie carrying gifts into a room full of young men and instruments and a shining silver girl whose voice shimmered on the air.

'Hi there, Carrie,' cried the young men. 'Thanks for your card. It's great.'

Feeling flushed and foolish and curiously unbalanced, Carrie showed them the cake and explained about boiling the pudding for at least two hours. They listened reverently with bowed heads. 'Wow!' they said. Then they carried the cake to the table moving the bottles and glasses back to make space for it. One of them took the pudding to the far end of the room, and put it down on the bare boards.

'Where it will be safe,' he explained.

Carrie had a feeling that it would still be there next Christmas Eve, covered with dust and spiders. The shining girl came over and threw her arms round her neck.

'Oh, Carrie, Carrie, you are so kind! Tone's just signed me up as his singer. I couldn't tell you before.

I didn't know it would happen. The gigs have only just come through. Oh, Carrie, Carrie, I won't ever forget all you've done for me.'

This silver swan was Claire! A Claire she'd never seen before. (Had she ever looked?) 'Who is Tone?' she asked, but knew even before Claire pulled him forward.

'Isn't Claire great?' glowed the green haired one. 'She's got a voice that's really, really great.'

Then all the young men and Claire swooped and dived about the room like swallows picking up cases and instruments and flew downstairs where they began to load their gear into a dented minibus. Carrie stumbled after them. In shock she took off her red coat and draped it over Claire's flitting figure.

Claire, you can't go like that! It's freezing, you'll catch your death!

Mother's voice! *Still* inside me!

'Tone's cousin's taking the house while we're on tour,' one of the young men told her, as he heaved the drums in. 'He's on his way now. He won't give you any grief. He's a medieval flautist and about ninety.' And he laughed, this youth, being all of twenty.

Carrie's heart cried out. Claire can't go, you love

her, she's been like a child, like a younger sister. But Carrie was running into her house, up the stairs into her bedroom, taking Claire's Christmas present from a drawer. She wrote a four figure cheque to go with it and on the card *Love, luck and kisses, Carrie.*

Don't blot it with tears, *don't*. Don't make her feel guilty. She raced back.

The minibus was gone. The street empty. The tears she'd held back filled her eyes. Slowly she turned and saw that Mother Christmas was wearing a red cloak. She looked as royal as a queen. Dashing the tears from her eyes Carrie saw it was not a cloak, but her red coat. *Oh!* Tears started down her cheeks, but she shook her head furiously, you silly Carrie to think that Claire needed a coat! She's found her love and followed her love and she'll be warm forever.

She went slowly in at her gate and up the path, not bothering with the coat, and wearily up the steps into the hall.

The two little candles were burning brightly. Still! They've been burning for hours. But you'll never get your third candle lit, little tree. Claire's gone.

She laid the present and the card on the hall table

and thought, what now? Ring up a friend? Open a bottle? Get drunk?

Carrie, Carrie, came her mother's voice, sharp as an east wind, *stop feeling sorry for yourself. Do something for somebody even sorrier.* Up to the surface of her mind shot the girl on the iceberg. Light poured on Carrie. She laughed out loud.

'*You*! Yes, you *shall* have space. I'll come off committees, refuse lame ducks, and let you *grow*!'

A bud of fire appeared on the topmost candle and flowered into flame.

Oh Carrie, her mother's shocked voice, *you selfish child. How could —*

'Mother,' laughed Carrie, 'lie down now and go to sleep.'

She listened for the rebuking voice, but none came. She picked up the little tree and warmth flowed into her. She took it out on to the top step and looked at the scuffed snow where Claire and the young men had swooped and fluttered and felt only gladness and hope.

The air began to quiver as though something was coming. 'Happy Christmas, Carrie,' whispered Carrie to her starved and growing self, as the first stroke of midnight laid its weight upon the air. A car came nosing round the corner of the Square carrying the medieval flautist (not ninety, not half that age). Across the park, the tramp came striding.

They made a strange trio, the three tall figures. The flautist unfolding himself from the car, the tramp holding her hand out for the tree and Carrie with her three bright candles coming down the steps to meet them. No wonder Mother Christmas smiled.

The Woman
Who Lived in Squares

THERE was a woman who lived in squares. She hadn't always. As a girl she'd lived in a straight line, between two other straight lines, her parents. Then she married and thought she was still living in a straight line, but the line was one side of a triangle. Soon after she found this out, her husband left her for the other side of the triangle and she was alone with a small son. Followed a terrible time. But she was a strong woman and one day as she stood in the kitchen, she opened her mouth and said aloud, 'I will live in squares. Squares are safe.'

She bought squared paper and a ruler, ruled each day into squares, wrote what she wanted to do in each square, and pinned it up. When she'd done a square, she crossed it off. The squares saved her. They disciplined the shapeless days.

'I'm ruling my squares,' she would say cheerfully if a neighbour called while she was doing it, or 'Well, nice chatting, but I must get on to my next square.' What she never noticed, though the neighbours did, was that the squares were ruling her.

She was small, quick and neat. Her son, sixteen, was a large, slow, loose-jointed lad who did not fit in any square, followed no line. His mother despaired.

One winter morning, when it was as mucky inside as out, she put on her red boiler suit, rolled up the sleeves and said aloud, 'First square, scrub the kitchen floor. Second square, wipe down the shelves. Third square, clear out the broom cupboard. Fourth square, have a cup of tea!'

She did the first square in twenty minutes. The red tiles shone like satin. She cleared the shelves, stacked the china on the dresser, had just wrung out a cloth in warm soapy water when the back door opened and the round red face of her son appeared, with snow on his hair, snow on his shoulders, like the morning sun breaking through cloud. Like the sun he beamed at her. 'Bus didn't come, Mum.'

He flung his scarf at the rack above the boiler, his gloves at the dresser. (He always put them on the dresser. She always took them off.) The scarf dislodged a tea towel, freshly ironed, which fell into the cat's saucer. The gloves sent plates spinning to the floor. Three broke.

'Oh! Sorry, Mum, I didn't notice.'

Spots of red appeared on her cheeks, splutterings broke from her mouth, but he was hunkering down on the floor, reaching for the pedal bin in its lair under the sink. It tipped as he pulled it forward and rubbish spilled over the satiny red floor.

'Leave it, leave it!' she screamed.

He rose to his huge height, turned to get the broom and knocked over the bucket of dirty water still standing on the floor. Rubbish floated on the flood. Fury burst from her.

'Sorry, Mum. Never saw it.'

He got the mop and mopped up, rinsed the mop, squeezed it dry and put it back. Then, painstakingly, he picked up every bit of rubbish and took the pedal bin out to the dustbin, leaving the door open and snow whirling in. He came back with potato peelings sticking to his boots and lumps of dirty snow melting on the satiny red tiles. He shoved the pedal bin under the sink, then picked up the kettle.

'Cup of tea, Mum?'

She couldn't answer. Anger was boiling inside her, escaping in snorts and sniffs and twitches.

'You look great, Mum. Red suits you.'

The anger went. She tried to hold on to it, but pleasure flooded her. He had a smile that would melt Medusa, with a dimple in his left cheek. He'll twist any woman round his little finger, like his father. But he was not like his father, and she knew that. She picked up the tea towel (it had drunk all the cat's milk) and rinsed it out in the sink.

'You can put my name in the pot.'

When the time came for him to leave school, she went to see the careers master. But, 'I cannot help your son. He has no idea what he wants to do,' said this baffled creature.

When she repeated this to her son, he was surprised.

'I'll do anything. I want to work.'

But there is no job marked *Anything* and some jobs require an animal cunning never specified in the adverts.

He came home with shining eyes. 'I've got a job at the Brown Loaf as waiter and washer-up. The manageress says I can earn two hundred pounds a week!'

Off he bicycled, but he did not earn two hundred pounds, he did not even earn one hundred. He got the sack.

She came back from shopping one morning to find him standing in the kitchen, chin on chest.

'What's happened? Why are you here? Is the Brown Loaf closed?'

He could hardly lift his head. When he did, his face came up like the rising sun, crimson with shame. 'I've been sacked.'

She could not believe it. 'Why?'

'I stood about too much and I ate the food left on the plates.'

He was always hungry, the big lad. Her heart was riven with pity and anger. His first job, his shining hopes. She could have whizzed down on her bicycle and scratched the manageress's face to ribbons.

'When there was nothing to do, the others ran about pretending to be busy, moving plates about, washing things up twice. It was a con, Mum, anyway. You could only earn two hundred pounds a week if you did overtime and worked bank holidays, and the Manageress kept *those* for her favourites.'

She threw her arms around him, and hugged him. Inwardly she prayed, dear God, make a square for him. Make a square for my son.

That summer he got a job putting up stands at the county show. He and a linguist from Belfast University worked together. The Irishman told him about Cuchulin, the Irish hero, and that *corgi* and *hound* have the same root *cu* meaning *dog*.

The two of them would stand, planks see-sawing on their shoulders, one yakking, the other listening, deaf to the shouting and the hammering.

'What are they like?' groaned the foreman. 'What are they like?'

The boy helped to put up stands for the cat and dog judging tent and was amused to discover that the cat benches had to be angled, so no cat could see another. If they did, it upset them. At the judging, he noticed that, while the dogs enjoyed being shown, the cats would have none of it. They walked down to the end of their cages and sat with their backs to the judge and refused to turn round. Good for you, mogs, he cheered inwardly, you know you're best.

Wandering among the tents one day, he tripped over

a guy rope, banged his head on a tent peg and saw stars. Rising groggily to his feet, his eyes fell on a placard, MEET YOUR STARS! I just have, he thought, well I will, and went in.

A woman took his hands and peered at his palms.

'A black cat will cross your path – and – no, that can't be right!' She dropped his hands and reached for her crystal ball. She took the cloth off and peered into its depths. 'Ah, yes. It is a black cat and it will cross your path and you will, you will –' She broke off. Frowning, she brought out a pack of cards and began dealing them out and turning them over. 'Well, you *will* meet a black cat and you *will* –'

'Will what? Will *what*?'

'Cut off its head!'

'Me? Never. I love cats.'

She got up. 'We'll try the leaves.'

She moved to the back of the tent and he watched her put three teaspoonfuls of loose tea into a brown teapot, take a kettle, singing to itself on a calor gas stove, and pour boiling water into the pot. She stirred the tea, put the lid on and called out, 'Milk? Sugar?'

'Please, one sugar.'

She brought him a cup.

'Whew! You make a powerful brew!'

'Drink it down, then give me the cup.'

He did so. She tilted it to let the last few drops trickle out, and silently, let him look in it. A large tealeaf cat stretched halfway up one side. On the other was a tiny tealeaf figure.

'If that's me, I'm very titchy.'

'You're not titchy, son. It's a bloody big cat.'

Five pounds lighter in his pocket, he left the tent and met the Irishman coming to look for him.

'Come on, mate, we've got to hose down pigs. They're dying in this heat.'

It was blazingly hot. No coolness anywhere. In the tents the heat was suffocating. In the pig tent, prize porkers were collapsing. Hoses with spray nozzles were thrust into their hands by a desperate stockman. 'Keep them cool, lads, keep them cool. I'm losing money.'

All morning they sprayed and sprayed, pink as the pigs, sweat glistening on them. In gasps the boy told the Irishman what the fortune-teller had said. The Irishman was interested.

'You get that in fairy tales, people turned into

animals. There's one where a prince is turned into a fox and the fox begs for its head to be cut off and when it is, suddenly, there's the prince again.'

'I couldn't cut the head off a living animal,' the boy said shuddering.

'In a fairy tale, the animal would beg you to.'

The next day was even hotter. More pigs died. 'I shall die,' panted the boy, 'if I don't get some air.'

He handed his hose to a Cambridge student who'd just entered, and went out. The air was so heavy with heat it was almost solid. The ground seemed to move up and down. He walked towards the beer tent, but had to stop halfway. He stood in the shade of a tent and lifted his arms to let the air get round him. A black cat burst from a tent a little way ahead and staggered about crying and trying to pull its head off, then fell to the ground motionless.

'Lord!' He ran towards it though the exertion made his head pound and his lungs nearly burst. When he reached the cat, he knelt down and felt round its neck. His fingers found a zip, but the zip was stuck in the thick fur. He took out his penknife and carefully pushed the point through the fabric and sawed a slit across the throat. At least that will let air get in. Then he rolled the cat half over and cut round to the back of the neck and managed to get the head off. He stood it on the grass and looked at the face it revealed. Crimson with heat and wet with sweat, it was still a pretty face. Thin black brows, long black lashes, short flat little nose, pointed chin. The eyes were closed.

He got up and looked into the tent the cat had burst from. Pyramids of pet food tins, posters of cats, dogs, budgies, parrots, leaflets – but nobody about. Restaurant tent, he thought, kitchen, and ran full tilt, heart trying to burst through his chest. In the kitchen Leicester University women students were washing up.

'Hey!' cried one, 'You are hot! Have a glass of water before you combust.'

She was the tallest girl he'd ever seen; a helmet of gold hair, eyes blue as snowshadows, face flushed to a pale rose, arms white as milk. She handed him a glass of water. He took it, but didn't drink. Instead, he gasped, 'There's a girl unconscious and –'

'I'll come. I have first aid.'

She grabbed a jug of water, shook ice cubes into it, picked up a cloth and strode out of the tent.

He led her between the lanes of canvas. Her stride matched his and she was a good inch taller. When they came to the figure stretched out on the grass she knelt down, dipped the towel into the water and wiped the sweaty face. The lips parted and she trickled water between them. The eyes opened, green as a cat's. The tall girl said gently, 'Now, drink. I'll lift your head. Little sips, that's right. Now, we get you out of this fur.'

She lifted her brows at the boy and he knelt down facing her and helped to get the costume off. She held it up in distaste.

'In this heat, this should not be worn, it could kill. Now, I must go. You bring these when you've finished with them.'

She flashed a brilliant smile, ice under blue skies, and strode off. The catgirl, for the cat was a girl, looked after her.

'Where did that come from? Are there still freak shows? The Tallest Woman? See the Giantess? Seven foot and fifteen stone, at least.'

'Six foot two and twelve stone,' said the boy, guessing correctly. 'She helped me save your li –'

'My head!' screamed the catgirl, reaching for it, 'Oh

my head! What have you done to it? You've ruined it. It's all cut.'

'I had to cut it to get it off. The zip was stuck.'

'It was hired, for God's sake. Jimmy will be furious. He'll sack me.'

'Jimmy wasn't about. I was. Where is Jimmy?'

'Lunch, of course. Where else would he be? But he'll be back. He'll see this and –'

'Give it here. I'll get it mended and bring it back first thing tomorrow. Tell Jimmy it was too hot, you nearly fainted and you've put it away. Unless he's an idiot, he'll believe you.'

His anger reached her. She looked up, saw his height, his good looks, and began to flirt, putting her head on one side, making her eyes sparkle and smiling deliciously.

'What are you doing at the show?' she purred.

'Hosing down pigs. They're dying in this heat.'

'Pigs!' She gave a shudder. 'How smelly.'

'On the contrary, they couldn't be cleaner or sweeter. Pigs are highly intelligent, love company and their manners are exquisite.'

He bent, holding the head in one hand and put the

empty glass inside it, draped the body over his arm and picked up the jug and cloth.

'I'll take these back. Goodbye.'

She scrambled up, pink spots in her cheeks.

'You stink of pig! That's what brought me round.'

He produced his dimpled smile and saw her waver.

'Goodbye, *cat*.' Accent on cat.

He marched off to the kitchen, pleased with himself. She'd got under his skin, but he'd got under hers.

The tall girl was back at her washing up, and how fast she washed up!

'Hullo! Why have you brought that dreadful thing? It should be burnt.'

He explained about Jimmy. 'She was frightened of getting the sack.'

'Aha! Her green eyes got you? How are you going to mend it? You are good with your needle?'

'My mother will. She's brilliant with her needle.'

'In this heat? For tomorrow, early? It will not be, I think, an easy job.' She saw doubt cross his face, knew she'd shaken him.

'Leave it here. Then it will not smell of pigs. Come back when the fair closes. I will come back with you and help your mother. With two it will be quick.'

'It's five miles, over fields. I walk.'

'Five miles is nothing. I can walk twenty.'

'In this heat?'

'In anything.'

Big-headed and bossy, not little and dainty and sparky, but it was a relief to be rid of all that nylon fur. He dropped the costume thankfully at her feet and went back to the pigs.

'The wanderer returns,' greeted the Irishman. 'How many beers did you sink?'

'None. I cut the head off a cat and it changed into a girl.' He told what happened.

'You smote and she is smitten?'

'I may have made an impression. We exchanged insults.'

When the show closed, he and the tall girl walked out of the show grounds and over the fields and over stiles and across the river and up the lane to his house, he carrying the head of the cat suit and she the body. She talked a blue streak, strode faster and, he discovered, was three years older, but none of this reached him for the catgirl had curled herself into him and her green gaze troubled his heart.

He became aware that he was being asked a question.

'I am Ingrid. You are –?'

'John. Johnny.'

'And your mother is?'

'Cottingham. Mrs Rose Cottingham.'

'Good. Now we can address each other. What will you do, Johnny, now you have left school? I am a geographer and a photographer. I shall travel the world photographing trees. I am in love with trees. What are you in love with?'

Green eyes, he thought, a pointed chin. Aloud he said,

'I'm wondering what square my mother will be in. I rang her, but she must be out. Must have been in her shopping square.'

'Squares are good. You know where you are with squares. But life is not all squares. Squares can disappear. Does your mother know that? Perhaps she fears that?'

The square was ironing. Scarlet with heat, streaming with sweat, reminding them both of the catgirl, Rose was ironing. She put down the iron with astonishment as they came in and grew even more astonished when

Ingrid picked it up.

'Stop! You are to sit in the shade and sip a glass of cold water, slowly. I will finish the ironing. I am a brilliant ironer. John will bring you a cold drink. He is a knight in shining armour. He rescued a girl from certain death this morning. He will tell you about it.'

And Rose found herself sitting in the shade, sipping from a glass which had slices of lemon twirling among ice cubes, while John sat opposite, can of lager in one hand, and told her about the catgirl.

'Didn't she thank you?'

'She was upset. Her boss hired the costume, I'd ruined it. She was terrified of getting the sack.'

'What sort of girl was she?'

'Tiny, a little flat-nosed face with great green eyes and a pointed chin. Light little voice, bit squeaky, but she was angry. Prettiest girl I've ever seen.'

Alarm bells rang all over Rose.

Ingrid came out. 'All done. Can I make you some food? There is a shop near? Do you like tinned salmon? Then we will mend the cat. John has explained? Do not be alarmed. With two it will be easy.'

Her long stride took her to the village store and

back in no time. Her quick hands produced tinned salmon salad with ice cream to follow, cheese and fruit. When it came to the cat costume, her deft fingers, following Rose's instructions, made the whole thing wearable in a couple of hours.

'There,' said Rose, 'we've made a fair job of that.'

'A Fair job,' Ingrid laughed, 'yes, a Fair job. I shall remember this fair, I think, all my life.'

She looked out at the garden where John was standing in the cooling dusk and her mouth stopped smiling and her eyes went sad.

'Poor John, he is thinking of green eyes.'

'What did you think of the catgirl?'

'Feline. The largest eyes I've ever seen. Green like a cat's and slanted like a cat's. They can kill at twenty paces.'

'You didn't like her?'

'Little women frighten me. Little pretty women. They flicker round you with their dagger eyes, their sharp little tongues, their stiletto laughter, all smiles and sweetness, and cut you to pieces, usually in front of people.'

There was a pause, then, 'My mother was tiny and

beautiful. She nearly died giving birth to me, my great lump of a daughter, she called me.'

Rose said anxiously, 'But now she's proud of you? So clever, at university?'

And so beautiful, she nearly said.

Ingrid shrugged, 'I have no idea. Neither has my father. We have not seen her for years.'

There was another silence. John wandered out of sight into the vegetable garden. Ingrid's gaze fastened hungrily on the tall barricade of runner beans. She heard Rose say, 'I'm little.'

'But also big.' Ingrid turned swiftly. 'Big heart, big courage, big strength. If you had to get into a cat costume, you'd make it. You'd make it breathe, you'd make it light, you'd make it *real*. Beautiful and sensible. Cats are beautiful and sensible.' She looked at Rose and the sadness left her face. 'You would make a lovely little cat, loyal and loving and beautiful.'

Lord, Lord, thought Rose in a panic, I'm going to cry! Don't let me, Lord, please don't let me. She got up quickly and went to the kitchen and mopped her eyes on the roller towel. The day's squares were staring at her. Someone had crossed out ironing. Ingrid? She tore the chart off the wall and threw it in the bin, pulled out the drawer in the kitchen table and took out a fresh sheet of squared paper and the ruler. With shaking hands she ruled one large square, wrote in tomorrow's date and GO TO THE SHOW and stopped, astonished. *I'm shaking, I'm – I'm – I'm in turmoil.*

She had never been to the show. She had never been to a fair. Her parents never had. Too expensive, they had said and, well, not safe.

Her son came in. 'Ingrid's gone, Mum. She said to thank you for the tea.'

'Oh, I was going to ask her to stay the night.' *Was I? Was I?*

'Oh well, anyway she's gone.'

Green eyes, thought Rose and her lips tightened. 'Ingrid's beautiful.'

'And bossy.'

'Decisive.'

'No, *bossy*.'

'Well, capable. She knew exactly what I meant when I was showing her how to mend that awful cat thing.'

'Oh, she's clever, and she knows it.'

'Well, she would, wouldn't she? Better still, she's

good. True. Solid. What she says she'll do, she will do.'

'Oh, she's square all right.'

Square! A square for her son! She smiled at his clouded face.

'Don't worry, love, things will come right.'

Early the next morning the boy set off carrying the cat costume carefully wrapped up.

Soon afterwards Rose set off, wearing a shady hat and carrying a few small neat sandwiches and a flask of water. It was going to be hot again, but the early morning was beautiful, the way was gentle and much of the footpath shady. How we lose the use of our legs, she thought. People go to gyms, to work out, but they don't walk. And walking's free.

The show bewildered her, frightened her, almost overpowered her, but she wouldn't let it beat her. There must be rhyme and reason to it. Asking questions, losing her way and finding it, she finally arrived at the pet food tent and went in. The first thing she saw was the cat costume. It was draped over a screen behind a table on which were pyramids of cat food tins.

A small crumpled man came forward.

'Where's the young lady?' she asked, pointing to the costume.

'Not turned up. I think she's scarpered. A boy brought the costume in. How he got hold of it, I don't know. Well, I can guess. She'd have it off in seconds for anything in trousers.'

'Who was she?'

'An out-of-work actress. Made a speciality, so she said, of playing animal parts, mostly in pantomime. Dick Whittington's cat, the goose in Mother Goose, the cow in –'

Words came out of Rose's mouth she didn't even know she'd thought.

'You need a much better cat costume! One that's wearable in a heatwave, not comic, *beautiful*. One that the children will love. I could design one, and make it, and wear it.'

She stopped aghast. His crumpled face smoothed wonderfully.

'You could?'

'Yes, and I'd make small stuffed dogs and cats, to scatter among the tins, for sale.'

His brown eyes shone. He looked as though presents

were raining down on him.

'Anyway, think about it. I'll come back later. But, just to show you –' She put down her flask and sandwiches, and went over to the cat costume, reached up and whipped it off the stand. Then she arranged it along the table putting a tin under a paw, another rolling away as if the cat was playing with them.

'That's fantastic!' cried Jimmy. 'I can almost hear it purr.'

'You could tape a cat purring and play it on and off.'

'Yes, yes! Look, you will come back?'

She walked out, head spinning with triumph.

Spinning so much that she cannoned into someone and reeling back, saw stars. Painted ones, on a notice,

SEE YOUR STARS!!!

And why not? Things are happening so fast. She went in, saw a chair, sat on it, put her hand to her head and shut her eyes.

A foreign voice. 'You all right, lady? A cup of tea? It's a fresh pot.'

Tea? A lifesaver, but would the cup be washed, and if it was, what in? Better say no, she thought and heard herself say, 'Yes!'

The tea had a hint of orange in it, very refreshing.

'Something wrong with your eyes, lady?'

Tears were trickling down Rose's cheeks. She smeared them away with the heel of her hand and saw the gypsy seated opposite her, knees almost touching hers, dark eyes watching. A clever face, thought Rose, a knowing face. A face that's never lived in squares.

'Tell your fortune shall I, lady?'

Never, thought Rose, such nonsense, but I'm sitting in her tent, drinking her tea.

'Please,' she said.

The gypsy took the cup from her, then took her hands, turned them over and began her spiel. Rose let her eyes wander round the tent. What a life to lead! Pack and go, pack and go, never knowing, never –

'…a long road, a strong road…'

I couldn't stand it, thought Rose. I'm a one place woman.

'…a true road, your road, up and on and –'

'This road you're on about,' said Rose, suddenly cutting into the spiel. 'Does it go anywhere?'

'Oh yes lady, into luck and out of luck, into storm and into shine, through sickness and health –'

'You make it sound like the marriage service!'

'I see a marriage, lady, no ring, but till death do you part –'

What nonsense! Rose jumped up. 'How much?'

'Seven pounds, lady.'

Rose counted out the coins, scolding herself, but went out buoyant. That tea was superb, how did she get the orange in it? I should walk into things more often. Now then, the kitchen tent.

She found it and saw Ingrid washing up like a maniac, but could not get near her, there was so much bustle. Well, the pig tent then and Johnny. Off she marched and found it and had a sight of Johnny spraying the pink sides of panting pigs, but he was too busy to notice her and the smell and sight of suffering drove her out.

She wandered round the show, astounded and excited. There were huntin', shootin' and fishin' people buying huntin', shootin' and fishin' things. There were splendid gleaming animals winning gleaming rosettes. There were show rings and stalls and tents; one was the Women's Institute tent. She went in and was moved at the beauty and skill of the craftwork and flower arrangements. The WI did refreshments. She sat down with a cup of tea and a home-made cake and found herself among neighbours.

'You walked!' they exclaimed. 'In this heat? There is a show bus.' They told her about it. 'We'll give you a lift home. We're not staying till the show closes today.'

Arriving home, she went up to the attic and dug out her old drawing board, her sketch pad and paints. She was buzzing with creativity. It felt like a huge fountain ready to burst out of her head, her ears, her eyes. Why did I never make a square for drawing? I won prizes at school. Because I was too busy bringing up Johnny, because Mum and Dad said art was a waste of time.

She sat in the vegetable garden in the shade of the runner beans, drawing board on her knee, and began to draw. When Johnny came home and found her, she said without lifting her head, 'Can you get yourself something? There'll be bits in the fridge.'

Later, he brought a tray of tea out for both of them and sat on the ground drinking and looking at the sketches lying on the grass.

'Cat costumes? For –'

'No, not her. She's gone. Jimmy told me.' She stole a look at his face. There was pain on it. 'Did you –?'

'Yes, in the beer tent, with her arm round the fat red neck of that potato king. She called me over, introduced me as Pig Boy – but the laugh was on her. He was interested and we talked pigs and he moved her arm away.'

He frowned at one of the drawings, laid his big hand on it and scrumpled it into a ball. 'Sorry Mum, but she's stuck on the inside of my mind and I can't get her out.'

She nodded, 'I know,' and sighed, her pencil flying over the paper.

'Last day tomorrow, Mum. Are you coming?'

'Yes, on the show bus, I can catch it in town.'

Next morning she caught the first bus from the village to the market town and joined a merry throng going to man stalls, help out or just look. Listening to the chatter and laughter, she thought, I'm learning, oh how I'm learning. I feel *new*.

Jimmy was over the moon when he saw her sketches.

'Could you really make this?'

'I could,' she smiled. 'I will.'

Early as it was, the day was already busy. 'C-could you, could you,' began Jimmy, 'the last day's always – '

'Stay and help? I could and will.'

That day was a learning curve like no other learning curve. Rose found selling exciting. She was quick at giving change. The customers and their pets amused and touched her. As she and Jimmy snatched a brief cup of coffee from Jimmy's thermos, he stammered, 'I suppose, I suppose you wouldn't –?'

'No,' she said quickly, 'no, I've Johnny. He's going to need a lot of support. There's my house and my garden.' And my squares, but she didn't say that.

He gave a sad nod. He's used to *no*, Rose saw, and felt bad but, life on the road! She shuddered.

The day drew to a frenzied ending. Tents were being taken down, gear stowed, animals loaded into horse boxes, kennels, trailers.

'Next year then, here?' Johnny said. His brown eyes pleaded. 'Make the cat costume and the toys, I'll leave you an address and I'll –'

A driver honked, trying to ease his trailer past Jimmy's van.

'Okay mate, I'll move her.' He turned quickly to Rose. 'Goodbye, thanks.'

A hot wind was whirling dust everywhere, stirring up

the animals and shortening tempers. Rose went in search of Johnny and found him outside the kitchen tent with Ingrid. Ingrid had an enormous haversack on her back and bundles stowed all over her. She turned to Rose.

'So, our ways part. I tell Johnny, come to Norway. Stay with my father and me. My father would love him. But no, he will not. So it is goodbye.'

She bent forward, the haversack looming over her head, and kissed Rose, it was like being kissed by a mountain, then she turned and strode off.

Rose stared after her, feeling bereft. Johnny was staring, leaning forward, watching the huge haversack and her shining gold hair move through the sea of bodies.

'She's gone,' said Rose stupidly and began to cry.

There was a creaking and a jangling behind them. A man stacking boxes looked round and shouted at them to move. They stepped aside hurriedly as the gypsy's caravan came up with the gypsy driving her skewbald horse. She flicked her whip at Johnny and pointed after Ingrid.

'Follow her, lad!'

But Johnny had already started forward and was now disappearing into the throng.

The gypsy grinned down at Rose. 'Don't wait, lady.

The road won't wait.'

'Road!' grunted the man, heaving boxes. 'Road'll be jammed. Much better wait.'

'No,' cried Rose, 'oh help me, help me!'

The gypsy reined in her skewbald, shifted her whip to her left hand and leaned her right down to Rose.

'Oh thanks, thanks,' gasped Rose. What *am* I doing? Climbing into a gypsy's caravan? But she knew what she was doing. Or part of her did.

Sitting high up by the gypsy on the jolting cart, she found Johnny's dark head in the crowd and watched it bobbing desperately forward, saw it draw level with the gold head, saw the gold head turn.

'Oh, thank God, thank God,' she breathed.

'And you, lady?'

'Oh me? Oh, put me down please, a little way ahead, yes here, just here, thank you.'

She jumped awkwardly down, looked up to call her thanks. The gypsy laughed and flicked her whip. The skewbald quickened its pace.

Rose fought her way to Jimmy's tent. If he should be gone, if he should be gone... but he wasn't. Pouring with sweat and covered in bits of straw and dust, more crumpled than ever, he was still stowing and packing and checking off items on lists. Every crease in his face seemed to smooth out when he saw her. She might have been a shower of gold. She flung her arms around him, he flung his arms around her. They clung and kissed. Two circles making one circle, Rose thought dizzily, we shall live in circles, circles of love spreading out until they touch the rim of the world.

The Girl who
Banished Selfe

A HIPPIE knocked on a front door. Three children opened it.

'Is your mum at home?'

The children shook their heads.

'Sure?' The hippie could hear someone moving in the sitting room and the television was on. He raised his voice. 'I'm from the commune in the woods. We make herbal medicine. We test the remedies on ourselves and they do work. I'll leave some with you, shall I? You tell your mum about them about when she comes back? Here's the price list.'

The children nodded, but did not tell him they had different mums.

'I'll leave some samples, the labels say what they are for. Headache, Listlessness, Clearing the Blood, and Constipation, and *these* four are very old medieval recipes. The one in the red bottle is *To Banish Fear*, the one in the green bottle is *To Brighten Wits* and the one in the blue bottle is *To Bring Beauty* and this little white bottle is *To Banish Selfe*. Don't cry, don't cry, please don't cry. There's nothing to cry about.'

He stopped dismayed, for the fat little girl, face like a paper bag, had begun to cry.

'I'll go now. You tell your mum about them, OK? I'll call back later.'

He took himself off and a slouching, big shouldered older boy came out of the sitting room and grabbed the red bottle.

'I'll take this. You'd better cut, Pudding, or Mum'll be back and you'll get it!' He went out of the front door, banging it behind him.

The black boy took command. 'The medicine ones we'll leave for our mums and we'll share the special ones. Betty, you have the blue one, Katie, you have the white one, I'll have the green. Don't cry, Katie. If your mum's back, say you were playing in the garden. You were playing in your garden till we called you to come and play with us. We won't tell on you.'

'Run! Wipe the mud off your shoes. Your mum'll never know,' urged the second little girl. Fiery red curls bounced on her head, her blue eyes had a slight squint, and her nose turned right up, but her smile made up for all three. 'Go on, Katie, quick!'

The fat little girl went blundering down the garden, sobbing and gasping, squeezed through the gap in the fence and panted up her mother's neat back garden and in at the back door.

Her mother was sitting at the kitchen table, drinking a cup of tea, while the slouching boy unloaded her shopping basket.

'And where have you been, my lady? Here's Tom left his books and made me such a welcome cup of tea.'

She looked hard at her daughter and her face sharpened.

'If you've been playing with those raggle taggle children –'

'She's torn her dress and dirtied it and look at her shoes!' In one rapid sentence, Tom diverted his mother's anger and dropped his sister in it. Katie began to shake, her mother made a grab at her, and her brother took himself off.

He was going to meet the Apes, the local gang. He was almost in it, almost. He was not much liked, but he was big and bigness was an asset. He took the stopper out of the red bottle, swallowed the contents, threw bottle and stopper into the gutter, and swaggered on.

Back at the house, Katie stood shivering in her vest while her mother stood at the sink, washing her dress and scolding her with equal vigour.

Across the road the other two mums had returned from the chip shop and were pouring the contents of the bottles down the sink.

'Good job we returned when we did! You could have poisoned yourselves, you silly muggins!'

'We only drank a few drops!'

'Good job you did! Those hippies go grubbing up toadstools and fungus, stuff a rabbit wouldn't eat. Now come and eat your lunch.'

And they dished out the chips.

The next year the red-haired child's mother packed her bags and went! The year after that the black boy's father took off. Neither were ever heard of again. In due course, a stepmother appeared for the red-haired little girl and, after a while, a stepfather for the black boy, though in neither home were the marital relationships very stable. There was a fair amount of flingings-out and comings-back, but the children stayed put. By the time

Johnny, the black boy, was sixteen, the last stepfather had gone and he was earning money to help his mother look after his siblings. By the time red-haired Betty was fourteen, she was keeping house as well as going to school, the last stepmother being not much older than herself and fairly hopeless.

No such goings-on had taken place in Katie's house, but there had been one terrible change. Tom was gone. On the day the hippie had called, he'd been hit by a car playing chicken and killed instantly.

The mother's grief was terrible, it was so like rage. She foamed, she fumed, she spittled, 'Those wicked boys, they killed him! They led him astray. They should be in prison, their parents should be in prison. They were responsible. Their sons should be dead, not my Tom.'

Her husband, feeling a mother's grief must be more than a mere father's, gave way to her in all things. Katie cried, but under the grief another feeling pushed up. Relief. It was wicked, but it grew. The bully, and the apple of her mother's eye, was gone. Now she was the only child.

The two grew close. Her mother was a devoted

churchgoer and an active, though selective, do-gooder. Katie went to church with her, helped in all her charities.

Life went on, the children grew up. Betty astonished everyone by being taken on as a salesgirl and model in an exclusive little dress shop.

'Why? Why?' people asked. 'She's not pretty. She can't be with that squint and that nose.'

But she was, she was, she had turned out enchantingly pretty.

Johnny, whom everybody had considered thick, startled everyone by going into business and getting customers. Soon he had his own business. Only Katie offered no surprises. She went to college and became a social worker. Well she would, said everyone, with that mother.

But actually, when her mother had asked Katie what she wanted to do, Katie had just laughed, 'Me do!' she said.

'You must do something with your life,' snapped her mother.

'My life!' laughed Katie, as though it didn't exist.

Her mother looked at her almost with hate. Square body, square face, complexion like boiled suet. How did

I produce a daughter like this? She herself had been a pretty girl, was still a pretty woman.

I'll slim her, she thought, and started Katie on a diet, but defeated it herself, because she was an excellent cake maker, famed for it. Her cakes took prizes, were queued for at the annual flower show in the autumn and the WI stall at the summer fête and this fame was nectar and incense to her. So, though she cut down Katie's breakfast, elevenses, lunch and dinner, when teatime came she could not stop herself cutting a moist, delicious wedge and handing it to Katie, purring, 'I'm sure a slice of mother's fruit cake can't do you any harm.'

Katie always ate it. She didn't mind how fat she grew. She didn't mind about her clothes, her hair, or whether her nose shone. She was a happy-go-lucky girl. The tears and nervousness of her childhood had gone.

A new rector came to the village, young, intelligent, and a bachelor.

'Your parish will find you a wife,' his bishop said to him and to the congregation when he was installed, and Katie's mother thought instantly, *Katie*.

'I don't approve of celibacy in parish priests,' she told him after one of their committee meetings.

'Find me a wife,' said he, smiling. 'I'm willing, but warn her. It's a full-time job. All hours, all days.'

She went home excited, a plan already in her head. Katie was up in her room turning out her desk, an overflowing wastepaper basket beside her.

'Katie love, I've just got back from the PPC committee meeting and stupidly I forgot to take my article for the parish magazine for the rector to see it.'

'He doesn't have to, Mum, you give it to Mrs Benson. She types the parish mag.'

'I know that darling, but the rector sees the articles before they go in. He has to approve.'

'Contributions don't have to be in till the seventeenth. Today's only the thirteenth.'

'Oh Katie, do something I ask for once. What's this?'

Katie looked over briefly. 'Oh that, I got it yonks ago from a – from a student. He said it was a medieval recipe *To Banish Selfe*.'

'Did you take any?'

'No, well, only a few drops. It tasted like spring water. Probably was spring water.'

'Katie, please, won't you –?'

'No Mum, *no*. I must finish this sorting.'

Her mother went downstairs, the little bottle in her hand, fuming. Katie is so selfish, she is a mass of selfishness. It would only take her ten minutes on her bike; well, twelve, it's quite a hill. She was still brooding on Katie's selfishness when dinner time came. How am I going to get her married? I want grandchildren, she's never even had a boyfriend. She stirred the soup, anger stirring within her. Katie's getting to look a right old social worker. Her glance fell on the little bottle standing on the windowsill among the bigger bottles awaiting the trip to the bottle bank. *To Banish Selfe*. The rector and his needs sprang into her mind. To banish self? She stirred more slowly. If it is only spring water, no harm done, if it isn't... well, only good! She stopped stirring, took the stopper out and held the little bottle upside down over the soup until the last drop had dropped.

'Why are we having tinned tomato soup while Katie's having your home-made leek and potato?' asked her husband at suppertime, making a rare complaint.

'Because there's just enough leek and potato for one,' she lied. 'I'll make my Greek chicken and lemon soup for you tomorrow. Don't worry, you shall have treats.'

Katie finished her soup and sprang up. 'Where's your

article, Mum? I'll bike up with it.'

'Finish your supper first!'

But Katie was out in the hall struggling into her mac.

'Where is it Mum? Your article, on the desk?'

'Yes – no – it's in a drawer, I'll get it, but wait, it's pouring.'

Her father came into the hall with two cheese biscuits layered together with butter and cheese. 'You're mad, girl, it's throwing it down. Eat this while I get the car out.'

'Thanks Dad, but no.'

She was gone, biscuits crammed into her mouth.

Her parents stared at each other.

The rector never forgot opening the door to her that wild night. The porch light shone on an enormous black figure, water pouring from it, hair plastered across a broad face, shining eyes, beaming smile, behind it the black night and the furious rain.

She stepped into the hall, dripping on the dogs who shook themselves. No, she didn't want the cloakroom. No, she wouldn't have a cup of coffee. No, she didn't need the fire, she was all right.

Mac off (he took it off almost by force), he steered

her into his study and into a chair by the fire. They talked church matters and parish needs and he found himself stimulated, amazed and drawn. She was clever, her ideas sound and workable, but it was the goodness that poured from her that excited him. He wished she would comb her hair and, presently, that she would blow her nose.

Eventually he reached for a box of tissues, saying with a laugh, 'My nose drips perpetually in this cold rectory.' And was relieved when she took one and used it. He wished he could offer a toothbrush in the same cheery fashion, but steeled himself not to mind the evidence of cheese and biscuits in her smile.

When she got back, her mother was ironing in the kitchen.

'Leave that Mother, I'll do it.'

'Don't be silly! Take those wet things off and have a bath, wash your hair, look at you. You've been ages. Did you talk?'

'Oh yes, he's nice.'

'Do you like him?' (Hurray.) 'Was he thoughtful?'

'Yes, I do. Yes, he was. He offered me a tissue. My nose was running. I didn't know!'

The next day Katie wrote to the county council,

who employed her, and resigned her post. Then she took all her clothes, except the ones she stood up in, to Oxfam and on the same day bicycled up to the rectory and asked the rector to employ her in any capacity he wished, for nothing. So he did.

She was enormously strong, got through mountains of work, was utterly selfless. Indeed, she seemed almost deformed in this respect, as though some necessary part of her that dealt with self had atrophied. She never washed, unless requested to, barely ate, barely slept. Her goodwill was boundless, her brain alert. The young rector found her impossible, extraordinary, invaluable. He could not think of her as a woman; she never thought of herself as one.

Many complained of her eccentricities. 'You must think of her as a saint,' he told them. 'The medieval saints were like this. Marvellous for their communities, but probably very difficult to live with, and likely very smelly.'

Her mother became distraught. 'You might think of me,' she complained, seeing her dreams go down the drain. 'Instead of all those others.' And learned never to make that remark again, for Katie immediately withdrew all her savings from the bank, booked a weekend break for her parents and sent them off with a new pair of pyjamas and a new night-dress, and stood on the platform waving goodbye till the train drew out. 'She should have kept that money,' fretted her mother. 'It was earning interest. We don't need a holiday in mid-winter.'

Katie's fame grew as her work grew. Soon she was working in a big city. Her mother received brief postcards, sudden gifts of flowers, but rarely saw her. When she did see, she was shocked. Katie was thin, dirty, unkempt. Sometimes her more forcible co-workers would persuade her into a bath, produce clean clothes for her, cut her nails, shampoo her hair. This they did out of love, out of worship almost, for Katie's goodness was the real thing, there was no taint of self.

People who were rather cold, rather hungry, rather poor and rather depressed felt worse when they saw her, but the ones whom life had defeated, who couldn't even kill themselves, felt better and loved her.

Johnny, meeting her by chance one day, was appalled.

'Katie, what are you doing to yourself? You're

almost a skeleton?'

His strong arm propelled her into a coffee shop, where he ordered soup, cheese on toast and coffee and made her eat.

'You must take more care of yourself. I'm a Christian, but I believe God means us to take care of our bodies. How else can we stay alive to serve Him? Think of yourself, Katie, you *must* think of yourself.'

The brightness left her face (there was always brightness under the dirt) and a look of agony replaced it.

'I can't, Johnny. I try sometimes, but I *can't*.'

A vague feeling of guilt attacked him, but he couldn't trace it to its roots. He ordered more coffee and some cake, but she could eat no more. When they rose to go, he took her thin face between his hands, kissed the grey forehead, 'Take care, Katie, take care,' and let her go.

'Where will it end?' wailed her mother, her face twisted in knots of anger and bewilderment. 'When will she stop?'

It ended where it had begun and stopped quite soon. Just before her seventh Christmas after she'd begun her life of service, Katie collapsed in the street and was brought home by ambulance.

With the help of a nurse her mother got the emaciated body into a bath and washed it. Got it into a clean nightdress and laid it between clean sheets, then brought up a bowl of broth and sat by the bed.

'Now, no more of this nonsense, you have to eat. Just a sip, now, then another. Come along love, to please me. Don't be selfish.'

'Oh Mother,' the voice was hardly there, 'I'm all right. Truly.'

She sipped and nibbled, but only crumbs and drops went down.

Her father raised her bed on bricks so she could see the sky over the trees and she lay always gazing at the sky. Once she whispered, 'It's like a miracle. I've almost got rid of me.'

The brightness slowly left her face, but the peacefulness was there to the end.

The funeral caused a stir. Reporters from the nationals, from abroad, television crews, all came. The bishop preached. But feelings were mixed. Many felt there was something extreme and unnatural in such a life, such a death. The bishop, while he praised her, wished he could banish from his mind, how she had smelt at meetings.

This second tragedy turned the mother from grey to white. The grief that had consumed her when her son died was red with anger. This grief was more like a grey fog. She went stumbling through it, searching. Did I do wrong? Have I been wrong? All my life? Have I not understood?

She did not wash or change her clothes, forgot to cook, to eat, sat for hours unmoving. Her husband tried to rouse her, but when he could not, went, worn out, to his sister's.

One day there was a slam of a car door and Betty came tittupping up on her spiky heels, her red hair bouncing. She rapped on the window and yoo-hooed through the letter box till Katie's mother let her in.

'Now then, Katie's mum, I've come to muck you out. I know you don't want anyone, and certainly not me, but life goes on, spring is here and this shutting yourself away isn't mourning Katie, it's mourning you. So let's start. You don't have to talk, but you do have to do. Cop hold of this.'

She thrust a basket at the dazed woman. Katie's

mother, clasping it, saw teatowels, cleaning things, teabags, a cake tin and a carton of milk. Betty slipped off her coat. Underneath she wore a lilac overall straining over a sticking out belly. She gazed round.

'Where'll we start? The kitchen? Let's go.'

Katie's mother followed. The kitchen was a slum. Washing-up in the sink, not washed up. The floor crunched under their feet. The windowsill was cluttered, the window smeary and bombed by birds. She sat down heavily on a chair and watched Betty attack the windowsill.

'There,' panted Betty, 'that's got the clutter off. Now you take this rubbish and throw it in the bin. Then take these dead plants, not that one, I think we can save that one, and pitch 'em on the compost. Then take this plastic bag of bottles and jars out to my car. We'll take them to the bottle bank later.'

Dumbly Katie's mother obeyed. When she set the bag of bottles down by Betty's car, the clinking jerked something in her mind. She bent down.

Good gracious, I thought I'd thrown that out.

She dived her hand into the bag and chased the little bottle all through the others and brought it out. I never did read the label properly, just tipped it into Katie's soup. She rubbed the dust off with her thumb and held it up. In the bright spring light she read *CAUTION. Only a very little of the mixture is needed. Too much can be dangerous.*

A timeless space held her. She saw the words *TOO MUCH* in capitals spreading all around her like ripples in a pond till all the questions in her mind were covered.

There was a tug at her arm. Betty was beside her, pushing a garden trowel into her hand.

'I've done the windowsill, the sink and the stove. Later, I'll do the floor and the window. But right now, let's do a bit of weeding. Weeding makes you feel virtuous.'

She plumped down by an overgrown flower bed and Katie's mother sank slowly to her knees beside her. A huge pain entered her heart and plunged and tore, then receded, leaving her with tears pouring down her face.

'Cry on the weeds,' said Betty gently, 'they don't like salt.'

'I made a mistake with Katie, Betty, a terrible mistake.'

'Oh mistakes!' Betty was weeding vigorously. 'The

mistakes we make for love!' She patted her belly with her ringless left hand. 'You made Katie a saint. She was happy. She'll never be forgotten.'

Gradually the tears ceased. Katie's mum wiped her arm across her eyes.

The sharp spring light sprang into her, stabbing her head, her heart, her blood, her bones until all the dark was driven out. She lifted her head and said aloud, 'Forgive me, Katie.'

Brilliant seconds went by, then she plunged her trowel into the bed and dug out her first weed.